WIDER WORLD

SECOND EDITION 2

CONTENTS

Unit 0	Welcome to West Green	2
Unit 1	Creating culture	6
Unit 2	People and personality	16
Unit 3	Animal life	26
Reading Time 1	Karen and the Artist	36
Unit 4	Cool tech!	38
Unit 5	My place, my space	48
Unit 6	Look after yourself	58
Reading Time 2	The Olympic Promise	68
Unit 7	Spending and saving	70
Unit 8	Learning for the future	80
Unit 9	It's only natural	90
Reading Time 3	Round the World in Eighty Days	100
Exam Time 1	Units 1–3	102
Exam Time 2	Units 1–6	105
Exam Time 3	Units 1–9	108
Self-checks answer key		111

Welcome to West Green

VOCABULARY
Family members | Possessions | Months and dates | Free time activities | Sports | School subjects | Skills and abilities

GRAMMAR
Possessive adjectives | Possessive 's | Have got | There is/are with some and any | Articles | Can/Can't for ability

0.1 Family members | Possessive adjectives | Possessive 's | Have got

GRAMMAR A Possessive adjectives

I	you	he	she	it	we	they
my	your	his	her	its	our	their

GRAMMAR B Possessive 's

Singular	my brother's laptop / Lena's brother
Regular plural	my parents' car
Irregular plural	the children's parents
Two words	Lena's mum's mother / Alex and Marie's house

GRAMMAR C Have got

+	I've got (have got) a sister. She's got (has got) a guitar. They've got (have got) a cat.	
−	I haven't got a brother. She hasn't got a sister. They haven't got a dog.	
?	Have you got a sister?	Yes, I have. No, I haven't.
	Has she got a brother?	Yes, she has. No, she hasn't.
	Have they got a pet?	Yes, they have. No, they haven't.

1 Complete the definitions.
  1 Your father's sister is your a u n t.
  2 Your father's sister's child is your c_ _ _ _ _.
  3 Your father's mother is your g_ _ _.
  4 Your mother and father are your p_ _ _ _ _ _ _.
  5 Your mother's son is your b_ _ _ _ _ _.
  6 Your father is also your d_ _.

2 Complete the sentences with the correct possessive adjectives.
  1 Hi, I'm Dave and this is *my* brother. _____ name is Jim.
  2 Hi! My name is Petra and this is _____ cousin. _____ name is Anna.
  3 Penny and I are sisters. _____ surname is Brown.
  4 My parents have got a car. _____ car is blue.
  5 Hi! Is _____ name Mark?

3 Choose the correct option.
  1 The (boy's)/ boys name is Gary.
  2 My *cousin's / cousins'* names are Tina and Rex.
  3 My *mum's / mums'* dog is Rusty.
  4 Pam is the *children's / childrens'* mum.
  5 *Harry and Jan's / Harry's and Jan's* house is in London.
  6 *Kai's brother's / Kais' brothers* bike is red.

4 Use the prompts to make sentences with *have got*.
  1 I / two pets
    I / a cat and a guinea pig
    I've got two pets. I've got a cat and a guinea pig.
  2 A: your cousin / a car / ?
    B: no / he / not
    _____
  3 we / not / a big house
    _____
  4 A: you / a sister / ?
    B: yes / I
    _____
  5 our teacher / a dog
    he / short legs
    _____
  6 my aunt / not / a big family
    _____

0.2 Possessions | There is/are with some and any | Articles

GRAMMAR A — *There is/are with some and any*

	Singular	Plural
+	There's (There is) a notebook.	There are some drawings.
–	There isn't a pen.	There aren't any books.
?	Is there a ball? Yes, there is. No, there isn't.	Are there any notes? Yes, there are. No, there aren't.

GRAMMAR B — *Articles*

- The first time we talk about a person/thing we use *a/an*, but the second time we use *the*.
  He's got *a* bag. There are a lot of things in *the* bag.
- If it's clear what person/thing we mean, we use *the*.
  Noah's in *the* park with his friends.

1 Complete the definitions with the words below.

> biscuits   bus ticket   drawings   headphones
> notes   sunglasses

1 You eat these. *biscuits*
2 You write these. _____
3 You draw these. _____
4 You need this to use a bus. _____
5 You listen to music with these. _____
6 You wear these. _____

2 Match words 1–8 with photos A–H.

1 [H] keys
2 [ ] some pencils
3 [ ] headphones
4 [ ] a phone
5 [ ] a notebook
6 [ ] some books
7 [ ] a pen
8 [ ] sunglasses

3 Make questions (?), affirmative (✓) and negative (✗) sentences. Use *there is/there are*.

1 *Is there* a TV in your bedroom?
2 ✗ _____ books in the kitchen.
3 ✓ _____ posters in the classroom.
4 ? _____ trainers in your sports bag?
5 ✓ _____ keys on the table.
6 ✓ _____ a game on the computer.
7 ✗ _____ a dictionary in the classroom.
8 ? _____ a pen in your school bag?

4 Choose the correct option.

We have ¹*a*/ *the* big house and ²*a* / *the* long garden. ³*A* / *The* house is very old. There's ⁴*a* / *the* lovely big kitchen. ⁵*A* / *The* living room is my favourite room. There's ⁶*a* / *the* big TV set in there. There are two bathrooms. ⁷*A* / *The* big bathroom is my parents'. ⁸*A* / *The* small one is for me and my sister. Near our house there's ⁹*a* / *the* small park. In ¹⁰*a* / *the* park there are lots of trees. There's also ¹¹*an* / *the* interesting museum and ¹²*a* / *the* sports centre.

Unit 0

0.3 Months and dates | Free time activities | Sports

1 Write the dates in words.
1. 11/02 = *the eleventh of February*
2. 15/06 = _____
3. 26/11 = _____
4. 02/04 = _____
5. 04/12 = _____
6. 13/09 = _____
7. 21/10 = _____
8. 30/07 = _____

2 Match words 1–11 with phrases a–k to make free time activities.

1	e	listening	a	films
2		playing	b	photos
3		spending	c	relatives
4		tidying	d	to the cinema
5		watching	e	~~to music~~
6		going	f	your bedroom
7		doing	g	a book
8		taking	h	video games
9		visiting	i	nothing
10		reading	j	time online
11		seeing	k	friends

3 Complete the sentences with phrases from Exercise 2.
1. I enjoy _____ to find information about sports and hobbies.
2. We like _____ and seeing the latest films.
3. Mary doesn't enjoy _____ her _____ – it's always a mess.
4. Dad likes sleeping on Sundays and _____ else.
5. Sara likes _____ and dancing to it.
6. I have a new camera because I like _____ at the weekends.
7. Marks likes _____ at the weekend and talking to them.
8. George enjoys _____ his _____, especially his cousins.

4 Complete the opinion adjectives.
1. I think this programme is b *o r i n g*.
2. I think this book is e__c__t_____.
3. I think this film is t_____ b__e.
4. I think this photo is g_____t.
5. I think this game is __u__.
6. I think this magazine is __n__ __r__ __t__ __g.

5 Match sports 1–8 with photos A–H.

A 8
B ☐
C ☐
D ☐
E ☐
F ☐
G ☐
H ☐

1. volleyball
2. swimming
3. football
4. running
5. hiking
6. tennis
7. basketball
8. ~~cycling~~

Unit 0 4

0.4 School subjects | Can/Can't for ability | Skills and abilities

GRAMMAR — *Can/Can't* for ability

+ I **can** cook.
  He **can** speak Spanish.

− We **can't (cannot)** dance.
  He **can't (cannot)** sing.

? **Can** you sing? / **Can** he speak English?
  Yes, I **can**./No, I **can't**.
  Yes, he **can**./No, he **can't**.

1 Look at the pictures. Complete sentences 1–8 with the verbs or phrases below.

~~act~~   cook   dance   drive a car   play the guitar
repair a computer   speak Spanish   swim

1 Dan *can act*.
2 Joe _____.
3 Ann _____.
4 Chris _____.
5 Helen _____.
6 Eve _____.
7 Michael _____.
8 Beth _____.

2 Make questions and short answers for the sentences in Exercise 1.

1 **?** *Can Dan act?* *Yes, he can.*
2 ? _____
3 ? _____
4 ? _____
5 ? _____
6 ? _____
7 ? _____
8 ? _____

3 Choose the correct question words below to complete the questions.

How old   What   ~~What time~~   When   Where   Who

1 A: (your first lesson) *What time is your first lesson?*
  B: At 10.30.
2 A: (your friend/now) _____?
  B: In the cafeteria.
3 A: (your brother) _____?
  B: He's fifteen.
4 A: (your favourite singer) _____?
  B: Sam Smith.
5 A: (your dad's job) _____?
  B: He's a policeman.
6 A: (your next holiday) _____?
  B: In August.

4 Look at the pictures and complete the crossword.

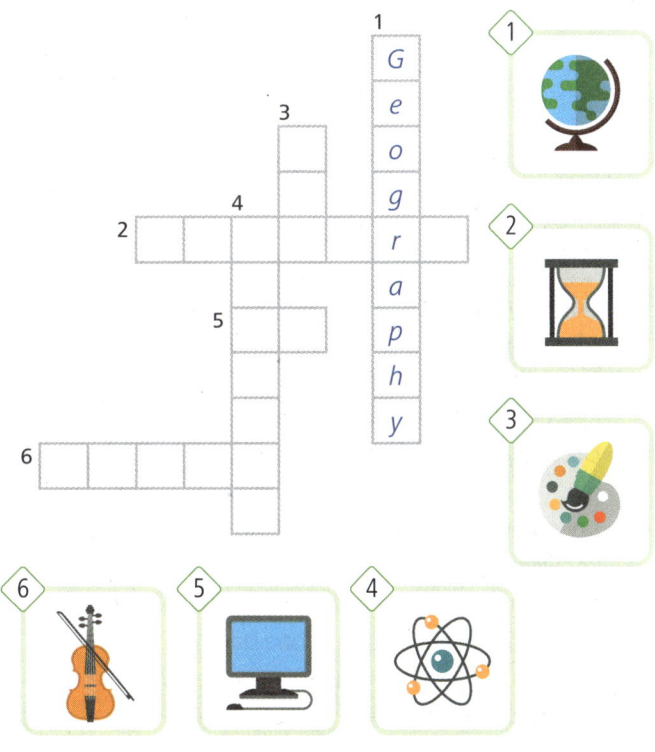

1 down: G e o g r a p h y

5 Choose the correct option.

1 *Have* / (*Are*) you sixteen?
2 *Has* / *Have* you got any brothers?
3 *Are* / *Is* there a café near your school?
4 *Has* / *Is* your mum got black hair?
5 *Is* / *Are* there any posters in your room?
6 *Is* / *Can* your sister drive a car?

Creating culture

1

VOCABULARY
People in the arts | Cultural activities | Creative hobbies | News and entertainment

GRAMMAR
Present Simple: affirmative and negative | Adverbs of frequency | Present Simple: questions and answers

1.1 Vocabulary
Culture

1 ● **Complete the words in the sentences.**
1. My friend Hannah is an excellent _d a n c e r_. She dances very well.
2. My sister is a great __u__i__i____. She plays the piano and guitar very well.
3. My favourite w____t____ is C.S. Lewis. He wrote *The Chronicles of Narnia*.
4. My brother's a p__o__o__ra__h____. He's got a cool camera!
5. I don't really like modern art, but I quite like old __r____s____s like Leonardo da Vinci.
6. I think Chris Evans is a very good __c_____. He's in lots of great films.

2 ● **Complete the text with the words below.**

director   guitarist   painter   poet   ~~singer~~

Hi Zoe,

Hope you are well. You asked about my family – well, everyone in my family loves art.
My mother loves music, but can't play any instruments. However, she's a great [1]*singer*. Dad plays a lot of instruments and he is a [2]_____ in a rock band. He's really good. My grandmother is a famous [3]_____ and knows many famous actors. She has a few awards too. My sister loves writing and wants to be a famous [4]_____ one day. Me? Give me a brush and canvas and let me paint all day. I hope to become a famous [5]_____, like Picasso. What about you and your family? Do you like art?

Write soon!

Tony

3 ● **Write the words for the definitions.**
1. You can see films in this place. c _i_ _n_ _e_ _m_ _a_
2. There's no singing. c_____
3. This is a modern type of music. t_____
4. This is a type of film about the future. s_____ f_____
5. This is a funny film about love. r_____ c_____
6. You can make these if you've got a video camera. a_____ f_____
7. This is a classical type of dancing. b_____
8. You can read this. n_____

4 ●● **Complete the sentences with the words below.**

ballroom dancing   ~~pop~~   rap   rock   salsa   street dance

1. *Pop* music is fun to dance and sing along to.
2. My little brother loves _____. He photographs dancers all the time!
3. Mary is taking lessons in _____ because she likes old-fashioned types of dance.
4. I love _____ music. The words express problems young people have.
5. Joe loves loud _____ music and he always listens to it in his room.
6. I want to go to _____ classes. It's a great Latin American dance!

Unit 1

5 ●● Complete the sentences with the words below.

don't   hate   interested   into
~~love~~   really

1 I *love* dancing rumba. It's cool!
2 I'm not _____ in comics – I like short stories.
3 I'm _____ acting. I'd love to be an actor.
4 I _____ romantic comedies. They're so boring!
5 I _____ like street art much.
6 I _____ enjoy drawing. I love my art classes.

6 ● **WORD FRIENDS** Match the sentence halves.

1 [d] I like reading   a pictures.
2 [ ] I like listening   b the guitar.
3 [ ] I like drawing   c selfies.
4 [ ] I like playing   d ~~poetry~~.
5 [ ] I like watching   e to hip hop.
6 [ ] I like taking   f fantasy films.
7 [ ] I like acting   g salsa.
8 [ ] I like dancing   h in plays.

7 ●● Order the letters and write the words in the sentences.

1 I like w<u>atchin</u>g (TWAGNICH) romantic comedies, but I prefer a_____n (NTOCAI) films.
2 I'm really into d_____g (NICNAGD) and I'd like to go to s_____t d_____e (RTEETS NADCE) classes.
3 I like t_____g (KINGAT) photos, but I don't like s_____g (RASHNGI) them on social media.
4 I love p_____g (NAGLIPY) the g_____r (RAGTUI).
5 I hate d_____g (DRWGANI), but I like w_____g (TWICGAHN) films.

8 ●●● Choose the correct option.

What are you into?
24 Aug 11:05

ann15

I ¹(really)/ very love books and I'm reading a ²comic / short story at the moment. The ³writer / director is an amazing ⁴musician / artist too and the pictures are great. There's a film showing the writer's life and I want to see it at the ⁵cinema / theatre. I'm also ⁶love / interested in drawing and ⁷taking / making photos. But I'm ⁸in / into dancing in plays too, so maybe I can be a ⁹dancer / photographer! Who knows?

9 ●●● Complete the text with the correct form of the words in brackets.

I really like ¹*dancing* (DANCE)! I love ²_____ (CLASSIC) music and I'm not a bad ³_____ (MUSIC). I can play the piano quite well. I don't like ⁴_____ (READ) books much, but I like short stories because they're quick! And I'm interested in ⁵_____ (WATCH) films on TV – if they're about famous ⁶_____ (DANCE)! I'm also into ⁷_____ (PHOTOGRAPH) and I like ⁸_____ (TAKE) photos of my friends in dance classes.

1.2 Grammar

Present Simple: affirmative and negative | Adverbs of frequency

GRAMMAR | Present Simple: affirmative and negative | Adverbs of frequency

+ I love hip hop.
  She writes poems/watches TV/studies classical music.
  We look the same.

− I don't read much.
  She doesn't understand art.
  We don't like the same things.

Adverbs of frequency (always, usually, often, sometimes, never) go after to be but before all the other verbs.

1 ● Complete the sentences with the affirmative form of the verbs in brackets.
1 My sister *likes* (like) hip hop.
2 We _____ (go) to a café after school.
3 I _____ (play) chess on Friday.
4 My teacher _____ (write) beautiful poems.
5 They _____ (speak) English very well.
6 My best friend _____ (live) in London.

2 ● Complete the sentences with the negative form of the verbs in brackets.
1 He *doesn't read* (not read) at night.
2 I _____ (not understand) modern art.
3 Carrie _____ (not listen) to rock music.
4 My mum _____ (not read) romantic novels.
5 I _____ (not win) when I play with him.
6 We _____ (not study) at the weekend.

3 ● Choose the correct answer.
1 a We never go to the cinema.
  b We go never to the cinema.
2 a I read sometimes short stories.
  b I sometimes read short stories.
3 a My brother is in his room always.
  b My brother is always in his room.
4 a I'm always interested in new songs.
  b Always I'm interested in new songs.
5 a Our mum usually goes to rumba classes.
  b Our mum goes usually to rumba classes.
6 a We are bored never in Mr Ty's classes!
  b We are never bored in Mr Ty's classes!

4 ●● Choose the correct option.
1 I never *does / do* my homework before dinner.
2 My sister sometimes *like / likes* listening to techno.
3 They *go always / always go* to bed at 10.30.
4 My favourite actor *doesn't / don't* act in comedy films.
5 She *never is / is never* at home before 8.30.
6 We *often play / play often* games in our English class.

5 ●● Order the words to make sentences.
1 like / Hannah / books / reading / doesn't / much
  Hannah doesn't like reading books much.
2 football / with / often / friends / I / my / play
  _____
3 understand / I / Spanish / don't
  _____
4 buy / online / I / clothes / usually
  _____
5 teacher / car / drive / doesn't / our / a
  _____
6 never / for / Tom / class / late / is
  _____

6 ●●● Complete the text with the correct form of the verbs in brackets.

I often ¹*go* (go) to the cinema with my friends at the weekend. We ² _____ (not go) in the evenings because we ³ _____ (do) our homework then. Our teacher ⁴ _____ (not be) happy if we ⁵ _____ (not give) homework in on time! We usually ⁶ _____ (watch) action films. I like romantic comedies, but my best friend ⁷ _____ (not like) them, so sometimes I ⁸ _____ (watch) romantic comedies on the internet at home. My sister often ⁹ _____ (watch) them with me. It's always nice to watch a film with someone else!

Unit 1 | 8 | I can use the Present Simple to talk about things which happen regularly.

On the Portal
Extra Practice Activities: Lesson 1.2

1.3 Reading and Vocabulary
Cultural activities

1 Read Mr Cooper's post. Mark the sentences T (true) or F (false).
1 ☐ This is the first day of the challenge.
2 ☐ He wants his students to share a photo only.
3 ☐ He often performs on stage.

Mr Cooper
Good morning! This is day 1 of the #culturechallenge. Please post a photo of yourself doing a cultural activity and say something about it in the comments. This is me performing on stage in last year's school play. I love acting, but I don't do it very often. I'd like to do it more.

1 Kiara
I like photography, but I don't think I'm very good at it. I usually go out every day and take photos of things in my local area. Do you like this one?

2 Graeme
I like creating new music. I play the keyboard and guitar and I often make new songs on my computer. I sometimes share my music online with other people, and they say nice things about it.

3 Marina
I really like writing short stories. I never write poems because I think they're boring. But I love writing short stories and I usually share them with my friends. Sometimes they don't like them, but they usually love them and ask me to write more. Would you like to read one?

4 Marco
I like making short films with my friend Dan. We make little models and take lots of photos of them in different positions. Then we put them together to make a film. Dan usually creates the story and I make the models, but sometimes he helps me make them.

I can understand a blog about cultural hobbies.

2 Read comments 1–4 in Exercise 1 and match them with photos A–D.

A ☐
B ☐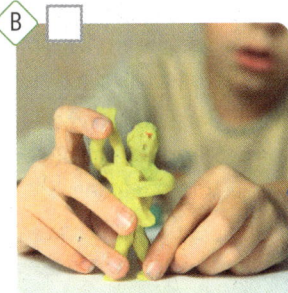
C ☐
D ☐

3 Read the texts again and answer the questions.
1 Who does their hobby in their local area? _____
2 Who would like to do something more frequently? _____
3 Who makes something with their friend? _____
4 Who shares something online with other people? _____
5 Who does something other people around them don't always like? _____

4 **WORD FRIENDS** Choose the correct option.
1 I love *creating* / *playing* art out of unusual things.
2 My brother often *performs* / *makes* on stage. He loves acting.
3 I like taking photos on my phone and *sharing* / *creating* them on social media.
4 I don't like *performing* / *playing* video games. I think they're boring.
5 Kyra *shares* / *watches* a lot of concerts on TV.
6 Jenny often *makes* / *plays* short films.

1.4 Grammar

Present Simple: questions and answers

GRAMMAR — Present Simple: questions and answers

?		
Do you go to West Green High?	Yes, I do./No, I don't.	
Does he work in London?	Yes, he does./No, he doesn't.	
Do they live in Paris?	Yes, they do./No, they don't.	
Where do you come from?	I come from Paris.	
What instrument does he play?	He plays the violin.	
How often does she see him?	She sees him every day.	

Time expressions (*once/twice/three times a week/month*) go at the end of a sentence.

1 ● Write the questions.

1. Q: Where *does he live*?
   A: He lives in London.
2. Q: When _____ school?
   A: I start school at 9.30.
3. Q: What _____ in the evenings?
   A: They do homework in the evenings.
4. Q: What _____ reading?
   A: My sister likes reading poems.
5. Q: How often _____ dance lessons?
   A: We go to dance lessons twice a week.
6. Q: What time _____ finish?
   A: The film finishes at 7.30.

2 ● Make questions from the prompts.

1. you / like / modern art / ?
   Do you like modern art?
2. your sister / speak / French / ?
   _____
3. Mr Jacobs / live / in a big house / ?
   _____
4. Jack / play / an instrument / ?
   _____
5. your dad / work / in the city / ?
   _____
6. your classmates / listen to / rap music / ?
   _____

3 ● Complete the short answers to the questions in Exercise 2.

1. Yes, *I do*.
2. No, _____.
3. Yes, _____.
4. No, _____.
5. Yes, _____.
6. No, _____.

4 ●● Complete the dialogue with one word in each gap.

A: ¹*Do* your parents work?
B: Yes, ² _____ do. My mum and my dad both work.
A: ³ _____ your mum work every day?
B: Yes, she ⁴ _____. She's a teacher.
A: ⁵ _____ she teach at your school?
B: No, she ⁶ _____. I'd hate that!
A: ⁷ _____ does she teach?
B: She teaches at Garfield High School.
A: Which school ⁸ _____ you go to?
B: I go to Minchester Academy.
A: ⁹ _____ you like it there?
B: Yes, I ¹⁰ _____. It's a great school.
A: ¹¹ _____ do you do in your free time?
B: I play football and I listen to music.
A: ¹² _____ often do you play football?
B: About ¹³ _____ or twice a week.
A: And ¹⁴ _____ you play an instrument?
B: Yes, I ¹⁵ _____. I play the guitar.

5 ●●● Complete the email with the Present Simple form of the words in brackets.

Hi Jenna,

I'm really glad you're my online English friend. Please write and tell me something about yourself! Where ¹*do you live* (live)? ² _____ (have) any brothers and sisters? ³ _____ (they/go) to school too or ⁴ _____ (work)? ⁵ _____ (you/listen to) music? What type of music ⁶ _____ (like)? What magazines ⁷ _____ (usually read)? ⁸ _____ (often go) to other countries on holiday? What are your favourite subjects at school? And ⁹ _____ (speak) my language? Sorry to ask so many questions. I'm really interested!

Best wishes,
Lucia

I can use the Present Simple to ask and answer questions about facts and routines.

On the Portal
Extra Practice Activities: Lesson 1.4

1.5 Listening and Vocabulary
Types of media

1 Match types of media 1–8 with photos A–H.

 A: 8
 B
 C
 D
 E
 F
 G
 H

1 talk show
2 phone-in
3 news headlines
4 documentary
5 soap opera
6 talent show
7 game show
8 ~~weather forecast~~

2 Choose the correct answer.
1 I often make videos and publish them on my ___.
   a message board   b sports pages   **c vlog**
2 I like watching ___. I learn about the world.
   a current affairs   b weather forecasts
   c talent shows
3 Before I go to the cinema, I read ___, so I know what other people think of them.
   a news headline   b sports pages
   c film reviews
4 Our school has a ___. We use it to discuss different things about school life.
   a sports page   b message board   c blog
5 I often watch funny ___ online with my friends.
   a video clips   b documentaries
   c game reviews
6 I always read the ___. I'm really into football!
   a weather forecast   b sports pages
   c news headlines

I can understand people talking about different types of media.

3 🔊 1.1 Read the survey. Then listen and match speakers A–E with questions 1–8. There are three extra questions.

A ☐ B ☐ C ☐ D ☐ E ☐

Take our QUICK ONLINE survey!

1 Do you think teenagers are interested in current affairs programmes on TV?
2 What's your favourite type of documentary?
3 Does anyone in your family watch a lot of sport on TV?
4 How often do you watch soap operas?
5 Why do people like watching talk shows?
6 Do you go to see films because of film reviews?
7 Do you want to go on a TV game show?
8 Do you enjoy watching talent shows?

4 🔊 1.1 Listen again. Match speakers A–E with comments 1–6. There is one extra comment.

A ☐ B ☐ C ☐ D ☐ E ☐

1 I think people sometimes have the wrong idea about teenagers.
2 I like learning about famous people.
3 I enjoy watching people who disagree.
4 I don't want people to laugh at me.
5 I argue about talent shows.
6 I think a programme can help people.

1.6 Speaking

Asking for and giving opinions

1 🔊 1.2 Listen and repeat the phrases.

SPEAKING | Asking for and giving opinions

Asking for opinions	Giving opinions
What do you think of this film?	In my opinion, the film is brilliant.
How do you feel about that song?	If you ask me, it's boring.
What's wrong/the problem with it?	I think it's great/brilliant/all right.
	I think it's terrible/awful/boring.
	I don't think much of it.
	It's no good.
	I agree/don't agree with you.

2 Match sentences/questions 1–6 with endings a–f.
1 b How do you …   a problem with ballet?
2 ☐ I think it's …   b ~~feel about hip hop?~~
3 ☐ What's the …   c with you.
4 ☐ In my …   d opinion, it's always the same.
5 ☐ I don't think …   e much of it.
6 ☐ I agree …   f exciting.

3 Complete the dialogues with the words or phrases below.

> ~~about~~   ask   I think   it's all right
> you mean   wrong

1 A: How do you feel ¹*about* this film?
   B: ² _____ the action film?
   A: Yeah, that's the one: *Power Time 2*.
   B: ³ _____, but I prefer the first one.
   A: Really? ⁴ _____ it's brilliant.
   B: I don't agree.
   A: Why? What's ⁵ _____ with it?
   B: Honestly? I think it's boring. If you ⁶ _____ me, it's the same story as the first film.
   A: OK, let's watch something else.

> great   much   opinion   think
> what   with

2 A: ¹ _____ do you think of classical music?
   B: I don't think ² _____ of it.
   A: Why?
   B: I ³ _____ it's boring. I prefer techno.
   A: Oh, I don't agree ⁴ _____ that. In my
      ⁵ _____, it all sounds the same.
   B: Not to me. I think it's ⁶ _____.

4 🔊 1.3 Complete the dialogues with the correct option. Then listen and check.

1 A: *c* classical music?
   B: I think it's boring.
   A: ____
   B: Do you like pop music?
   A: Yes, ____
   B: I agree. It's great.

a I agree.
b I think it's cool.
c How do you feel about

2 A: Do you like this sitcom?
   B: ____ .
   A: Yeah, that's the one. What do you think of it?
   B: ____
   A: Really? I don't think much of it.
   B: ____
   A: Honestly? I just don't think it's funny.
   B: ____

a Why? What's wrong with it?
b You mean *King of Secrets*?
c I don't agree. If you ask me, it's really funny.
d I think it's really funny.

Unit 1   12   I can ask for and give opinions.

On the Portal
Extra Practice Activities: Lesson 1.6

1.7 Writing
A personal introduction

1 Read the information about Ella on her webpage. Then read her personal introduction and complete the information.

Ella
Totton,
Southampton,
England
Romantic ♥

LIST OF STORIES
▶ The red table ▶ Another Monday ▶ Where are you?

About me
My name is Ella Myers and I'm fifteen. I'm from London and I live in Totton. It's a town near Southampton. I'm British. I have one sister and two brothers and I go to Totton High School. I love Art, English and History.

I like rock and pop music and my favourite band is *One Republic*. But I really love books. My favourite books are *The Fault in Our Stars* and *The Hunger Games*.

In my free time I play tennis and I write short stories. I write one or two pages every day. You can read some of them on my webpage. Tell me if you like them!

Name:	Ella ¹*Myers*
Age:	2 _____
Family:	3 _____
Lives in:	4 _____
From:	5 _____
Nationality:	British
Studies at:	6 _____
Favourite subjects:	7 _____
Music:	8 _____
Favourite band:	9 _____
Books:	10 _____
Likes:	11 _____ playing tennis

2 Read sentences 1–5 and mark P (personal), H (hobbies/interests) or R (routines).
1 [P] I have one sister and two brothers.
2 [ ] I go to school by bus every day.
3 [ ] I'm into books.
4 [ ] I live in Totton.
5 [ ] I play tennis. I'm really good at it.

3 Complete the sentences with the words below.

| favourite | from | home town |
| into | ~~old~~ | outside |

1 I'm fifteen years *old*. I come _____ London.
2 My _____ is Totton.
3 I'm really _____ books.
4 My _____ hobby is writing.
5 _____ school I like playing sports.

4 Match 1–5 with a–e.
1 [b] school subjects
2 [ ] at the beginning of a sentence
3 [ ] names of people and places
4 [ ] countries and nationalities
5 [ ] the personal pronoun

a Ella, Totton, Southampton
b ~~Art, History, English~~
c I
d My, It's, But, In, You, Tell
e British, London

WRITING TIME

5 Write a personal introduction for one of your friends.

1 Find ideas
Make notes about their:
• personal details.
• favourite school subjects.
• interests and hobbies.

2 Plan and write
• Organise your ideas into paragraphs. Use Ella's text to help you.
• Write a draft personal introduction.

3 Check
• Check language: is the spelling (capital letters) correct?
• Check grammar: are most verbs in the Present Simple?
• Write the final version of your personal introduction.

I can write a personal introduction.

My Language File

WORDLIST 🔊 1.4

People in the arts
- actor (n) _____
- artist (n) _____
- dancer (n) _____
- director (n) _____
- guitarist (n) _____
- musician (n) _____
- painter (n) _____
- photographer (n) _____
- poet (n) _____
- singer (n) _____
- writer (n) _____

Cultural activities
- action film (n) _____
- animated film (n) _____
- ballet (n) _____
- ballroom dancing (n) _____
- classical music (n) _____
- comic (n) _____
- fantasy film (n) _____
- hip hop (n) _____
- novel (n) _____
- painting (n) _____
- photo (n) _____
- picture (n) _____
- poem (n) _____
- pop (n) _____
- rap (n) _____
- rock (n) _____
- romantic comedy (n) _____
- rumba (n) _____
- salsa (n) _____
- science fiction (sci-fi) film (n) _____
- short story (n) _____
- street art (n) _____
- street dance (n) _____
- techno (n) _____

Word friends (creative hobbies)
- act in a play _____
- act in a (short) film _____
- dance salsa _____
- draw pictures _____
- listen to (rock) music _____
- play the guitar _____
- read poetry _____
- take selfies _____
- watch (fantasy) films _____

Word friends (cultural activities)
- create art _____
- make short films _____
- perform on stage _____
- play video games _____
- share something on social media _____
- watch concerts _____
- watch videos _____

News and entertainment
- blog (n) _____
- current affairs (n) _____
- documentary (n) _____
- film review (n) _____
- game review (n) _____
- game show (n) _____
- message board (n) _____
- news headline (n) _____
- phone-in (n) _____
- reality show (n) _____
- soap opera (n) _____
- sports page (n) _____
- talent show (n) _____
- talk show (n) _____
- video clip (n) _____
- vlog (n) _____
- weather forecast (n) _____

Extra words
- awful (adj) _____
- be afraid of _____
- be interested in _____
- be into _____
- be mad about _____
- brilliant (adj) _____
- cinema (n) _____
- cool (adj) _____
- creative work (n) _____
- culture (n) _____
- drums (n) _____
- enjoy (v) _____
- famous (adj) _____
- go dancing _____
- great (adj) _____
- hate (v) _____
- like (v) _____
- love (v) _____
- make animations _____
- news (n) _____
- newspaper (n) _____
- opinion (n) _____
- orchestra (n) _____
- paint (v, n) _____
- photography (n) _____
- programme (n) _____
- routine (n) _____
- share interests _____
- sing (v) _____
- (social) media (n) _____
- song (n) _____
- take part in _____
- take photos _____
- terrible (adj) _____
- theatre (n) _____

Sounds good!
- You mean … ? _____
- Honestly? _____

MY LANGUAGE NOTES

My favourite words/expressions from this unit

Self-check

Vocabulary

1 Complete the words in the sentences.
1. My brother reads c_____ every day. He likes the artwork.
2. I don't enjoy c_____ music like Mozart or Beethoven.
3. My favourite a_____ is Chris Evans.
4. I often watch r_____ comedies where people are in love.
5. A lot of children love watching a_____ films like *Minions* or *How to Train Your Dragon*.
6. My sister wants to go to Cuba to learn s____ dancing.

2 Complete the sentences with the words below.

> drawing   listening   playing   reading
> taking   watching

1. We have a computer, but I hate _____ games on it.
2. My dad is really into _____ to old music.
3. My mum doesn't really like _____ selfies.
4. I like _____ reviews about new films.
5. Our family loves _____ soap operas together.
6. I don't like _____ pictures in Art at school.

3 Choose the correct option.
1. I think *phone-ins / soap operas* are funny – you always hear some strange people calling!
2. You can post and find jobs on the *message board / sports page*.
3. *Video clips / Current affairs* programmes are useful to learn what is happening in the world at the moment.
4. The *talk shows / news headlines* today are about the earthquake in Japan.
5. Let's watch the *weather forecast / soap opera* before we decide on what to do tomorrow.
6. I love watching *soap operas / documentaries* about wild animals.
7. I can watch short *video clips / news headlines* and dance for hours!
8. I hate *weather forecast / reality shows*. They are boring.

Grammar

4 Order the words to make questions.
1. you / where / live / do / ?
   _____
2. work / day / your / every / dad / does / ?
   _____
3. do / many / have / lessons / English / a week / you / how / ?
   _____
4. do / you / Saturday / swimming / go / every / ?
   _____
5. do / how / photos / you / take / often / ?
   _____

5 Match questions 1–5 in Exercise 4 with answers a–e below.
a ☐ Every day.   d ☐ No, he doesn't.
b ☐ Yes, I do.   e ☐ In London.
c ☐ Three.

6 Complete the sentences with the Present Simple form of the verbs in brackets.
1. I _____ (not like) documentaries.
2. _____ (you/want) to go to the cinema?
3. My friend _____ (not live) near me.
4. Jack _____ (not speak) English and French.
5. Mr Lee usually _____ (give) essays to write.

Speaking

7 Complete the dialogue with one word in each gap.
A: [1]_____ do you feel about street dance?
B: Oh, I think it's terrible!
A: Really? What's the [2]_____ with it?
B: Well, in my [3]_____, it's just awful.
A: I don't agree with you. If you [4]_____ me, it's cool.
B: Well, I think it's no [5]_____. I prefer ballet.
A: Yeah, it's all right, but it's a bit boring.

YOUR SCORE

Vocabulary: __/20   Speaking: __/5
Grammar: __/15   **Total:** __/40

People and personality

2

VOCABULARY
Clothes and accessories | Adjectives to describe clothes and accessories | Adjectives with -ing/-ed | Personality adjectives

GRAMMAR
Present Continuous | Present Simple and Present Continuous

2.1 Vocabulary
Clothes

1 ● Complete the table with the words below.

> baseball cap ~~belt~~ coat glasses gloves handbag ~~hoodie~~ jacket necklace scarf sweater top tracksuit trainers underwear uniform

Clothes	Accessories
hoodie	belt

2 ● Choose the correct answer.
1 I usually wear ___ at the weekends when I go out with my friends.
   a a uniform   b a fancy-dress costume   (c) jeans
2 I don't really like wearing ___, but I need to wear one for my sister's wedding.
   a tracksuits   b dresses   c glasses
3 My dad works in a bank and he wears a white ___ to work.
   a hoodie   b shorts   c shirt
4 I've got two cool ___ from the USA with my name on them.
   a shoes   b T-shirts   c jeans
5 It's hot, so I need my ___.
   a shorts   b shoes   c boots
6 I like wearing ___ in summer to keep cool.
   a glasses   b hats   c costumes
7 I'm wearing a Superman ___ to the party.
   a baseball cap   b costume   c handbag
8 Don't forget your ___. It's cold outside.
   a handbag   b necklace   c scarf

3 ●● Write the words for the definitions.
1 You wear this to keep warm.
   s w _e_ _a_ _t_ _e_ _r_
2 You wear this round your neck.
   n_ _ _ _ _ _ _ _
3 You wear this under your clothes.
   u_ _ _ _ _ _ _ _
4 You wear this when you play sport.
   t_ _ _ _ _ _ _
5 You often wear these on your feet.
   t_ _ _ _ _ _ _
6 You wear these in the summer when it's hot.
   s_ _ _ _ _ _

4 ●● Read the sentences and write the words.
1 I love wearing these in my ears when I go to a party. _earrings_
2 I wear this round my neck. _____
3 I can wear this over my shirt at work. _____
4 They keep my hands warm in winter. _____
5 In the summer it keeps my head cool when I do sport. _____
6 We wear these on our feet every day. _____

5 ●● Match sentences 1–6 with a–f.
1 [e] This T-shirt is very baggy.
2 [   ] I wash these jeans a lot.
3 [   ] I like wearing this cotton top.
4 [   ] Can I borrow your woolly gloves?
5 [   ] I don't want a striped jacket.
6 [   ] These shoes are real leather.

a I prefer a plain one.
b Now they're really tight.
c It's cold outside.
d That's why they're expensive.
e ~~It's because it's my big sister's.~~
f It's cool in the summer.

Unit 2 16

6 ●● Choose the correct answer.
1. Which item can we NOT use with *baggy*?
   a trousers b sweater **c handbag**
2. Which item can we NOT use with *leather*?
   a boots b glasses c belt
3. Which item can we NOT use with *woolly*?
   a trainers b sweater c hat
4. Which item can we NOT use with *striped*?
   a dress b top c necklace
5. Which item can we NOT use with *tight*?
   a T-shirt b shoes c earrings
6. Which item can we NOT use with *checked*?
   a glasses b shirt c jacket

7 ●● Complete the crossword.

Across
3. not plain or checked
5. It's pretty and you wear it round your neck.
8. It's usually leather and you wear it round your jeans.
9. You wear them when you go running.
10. the opposite of baggy

Down
1. These trousers are usually blue.
2. You wear it over a shirt.
4. You can wear it when you train.
6. It's a warm top.
7. Wear it round your neck when it's cold.
8. not tight

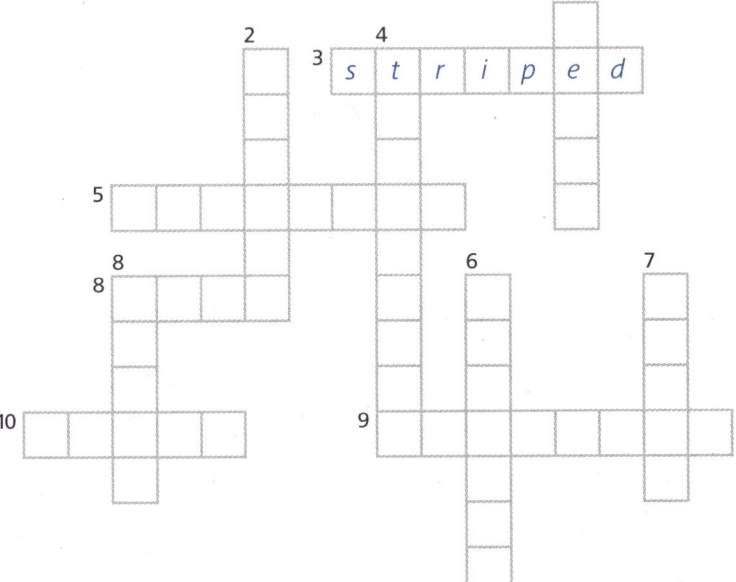

I can talk about clothes.

8 ●●● Complete the words in the text.

Kate's Clothes

Do you want something new to wear at the weekend or for that special party?

Come along to our new shop in the Lake Mall for clothes and ¹a c c e s s o r i e s. We sell everything from casual clothes like ² _e_ _ s and T-shirts, to dresses and even ³ _ s _ _ m _ _ for those fun parties!
Do you need sports gear? We sell comfortable ⁴ _ _ a _ e _ s for your feet and ⁵ _r_ _ _ s _ _ _ s for your training.
All our clothes are modern – if ⁶ _ h _ _ k _ d shirts are in fashion you can find them here.
We have both bright and ⁷ _ _ _ _ k colours. Perhaps this year it's ⁸ _ t _ _ _ e _ jackets? Look for them here! Would you like some ⁹ l _ _ _ _ h _ _ _ boots? We have them.
A warm ¹⁰ _ o _ _ _ e for when it's cold and windy outside? We've got a nice ¹¹ l _ _ _ _ _ _ blue one and many others.
We've got lots. Pretty gold earrings or a silver ¹² _ _ c _ _ a _ _ ?
Right here!

See you soon!

2.2 Grammar

Present Continuous

GRAMMAR Present Continuous

+ I'm leaving now.
  He's making some toast.
  They're looking at you.

− I'm not laughing.
  He isn't wearing a costume.
  They aren't talking.

? Are you coming? / Yes, I am./No, I'm not.
  Is he going home? / Yes, he is./No, he isn't.
  Are they eating? / Yes, they are./No, they aren't.
  Why are you laughing?

1 ● Complete the sentences with the Present Continuous form of the verbs below.

cry   drink   eat   lie   listen   ride   ~~take~~   talk

1 The woman *is taking* a photo.
2 The man _____ coffee.
3 Two children _____ their bikes.
4 The teenage girl _____ on her phone.
5 The old lady _____ a sandwich.
6 The teenage boy _____ to music.
7 The dog _____ on the ground.
8 The baby _____ – it's hungry again!

2 ● Rewrite the sentences in the negative form.
1 I'm waiting for Paolo.
   I'm not waiting for Paolo. I'm waiting for Brad.
2 They're studying French.
   _____
   They're studying Spanish.
3 She's wearing jeans.
   _____
   She's wearing trousers.
4 You're eating a chicken sandwich.
   _____
   You're eating a tomato sandwich.
5 We're watching the news.
   _____
   We're watching a talk show.
6 He's going to town.
   _____
   He's going to work.

3 ● Order the words to make questions.
1 new / wearing / dress / you / a / are / ?
   Are you wearing a new dress?
2 is / shouting / the / teacher / why / ?
   _____
3 the / what / doing / are / boys / ?
   _____
4 are / where / going / you / ?
   _____
5 us / Elise / here / is / meeting / ?
   _____

4 ●● Match questions 1–5 with answers a–e.
1 **b** Where are you going?
2 ☐ What are you reading?
3 ☐ Marie isn't coming with us. Why?
4 ☐ Are your friends swimming today?
5 ☐ Why is your teacher talking to Frank?

a He isn't working very hard these days.
b ~~We're walking into town.~~
c No, they aren't. They're playing tennis.
d My friend's fashion magazine.
e She's waiting for Mike.

5 ●●● Complete the dialogue with the correct forms of the verbs below.

~~do~~   do   eat   enjoy   shut   watch   write

A: Hi! How are you?
B: I'm good, thanks. What ¹*are you doing*?
A: Not much. I'm at my computer.
B: ² _____ emails?
A: No, I'm not. I ³ _____ my History homework. It's boring. And you?
B: I ⁴ _____ a reality show on TV with my sister and we ⁵ _____ cake.
A: ⁶ _____ the show?
B: No, I'm not. It's boring. Let's go for a walk after dinner. We can ride our bikes.
A: That's a great idea! I ⁷ _____ down my computer now!

Unit 2 | 18 | I can use the Present Continuous to talk about things that are happening now.

On the Portal
Extra Practice Activities: Lesson 2.2

2.3 Reading and Vocabulary
Festivals

1 Read the introduction to the article and answer the questions.
1 What do people celebrate in Argentina on 30 July?
  _____
2 What two things are people doing to celebrate it?
  _____

2 Read the article again and answer the questions.
1 Who throws water at people during Songkran? _____
2 What does Songkran traditionally celebrate? _____
3 How does Manisha describe what people look like? _____
4 What is in the sky in Albuquerque?
  _____
5 What can people see on Bondi beach?
  _____

How and what are you celebrating?

It's 30 July and in Argentina they're celebrating 'Friend's Day'. Friends are coming together and some of them are giving each other presents. It's a popular celebration here in Argentina, but what about other celebrations around the world?

'Today in Thailand we're having a big water fight! It's the Songkran Water festival. Everyone throws water at each other in the street for three days! We do it to celebrate the traditional Thai New Year. At the moment many people are also travelling because they want to spend this festival time with their families. They are also trying to stay dry!'
Dao

Manisha

'If you want to stay clean then don't come to Delhi at the moment. It's the Holi festival of colours, and people are throwing coloured powder at everyone in the street! There are many different reasons why people celebrate Holi, but it's mostly to be happy about good things in the world. We're laughing and having lots of fun. The people look beautiful too, I think.'

'I'm in Albuquerque in the USA, and today I'm at the huge balloon fiesta with my friends. Lots of people are throwing balloons in the air. They are all different shapes, sizes and colours. The sky looks really cool!'

Jay

Brett

'Welcome to the Sculpture by the Sea event. Once a year, local artists show their sculptures along 2 km of Bondi beach, a famous beach in Sydney. People are out with their families looking at the art and visiting local cafés. It's a brilliant way to spend a summer's evening.'

3 Match comments 1–8 with sentences a–h.
1 [c] I don't sleep very well.
2 [ ] This book isn't interesting at all!
3 [ ] I can hear a terrible noise outside.
4 [ ] My computer isn't working – again!
5 [ ] My dad is singing in front of my friends.
6 [ ] We're going on holiday.
7 [ ] I'm watching a documentary.
8 [ ] I'm just sitting in the sun with my book.

a It's interesting.   e I'm relaxed.
b I'm embarrassed.   f It's annoying.
c ~~I'm tired.~~   g I'm frightened.
d It's boring.   h It's exciting.

4 Choose the correct option.
1 When my brother tells a joke it's *embarrassed* / (*embarrassing*)!
2 James works from 6.30 a.m. until 7.30 p.m. His job is *tired* / *tiring*.
3 My sister often takes my clothes without asking. I get very *annoying* / *annoyed*.
4 I love the new horror film – it's very *frightened* / *frightening*.
5 Jake doesn't like romantic films. He gets *boring* / *bored* when he watches one.

I can understand an article about festivals.

2.4 Grammar

Present Simple and Present Continuous

GRAMMAR — Present Simple and Present Continuous

- **Present Simple**
  Facts, habits and routines
  I usually have breakfast at lunchtime.

- **Present Continuous**
  Things happening at the moment of speaking
  We are walking up a mountain.

  Things happening around now but maybe not at the moment of speaking.
  This week my parents are doing some work on the house.

1 ● Decide if the verbs in the sentences show facts (F), a routine (R), something happening during a period of time (P), or something happening right now (N).

1. [F] My mum works in a hospital.
2. [ ] She always gets up at 6.30 and takes a taxi to work.
3. [ ] Today she isn't feeling very well, so she's staying at home.
4. [ ] At the moment she's sitting in bed and sending some emails.
5. [ ] She has friends in lots of different countries.
6. [ ] She's working with a new team of doctors this week.
7. [ ] She usually finishes work at 6.00.
8. [ ] Oh dear – the phone is ringing. Perhaps it's the hospital.

2 ● Complete the sentences with the correct present forms of the underlined verbs.

1. I usually <u>have</u> cereal for breakfast. Today, I*'m having* eggs and toast.
2. Mariah doesn't always <u>come</u> to extra Maths classes after school. She _____ this week because her marks are getting worse!
3. It always _____ when I'm on holiday and look – it's <u>raining</u> now!
4. I know you often <u>play</u> tennis. _____ you _____ this week?
5. My friend _____ to school again – she <u>walks</u> to school every morning.
6. My brother usually <u>watches</u> game shows, but tonight he _____ a soap opera.

3 ●● Match the sentence halves.

1. [c] Cathy doesn't usually go to bed late,
2. [ ] She really enjoys soap operas,
3. [ ] She knows a lot of languages,
4. [ ] She usually goes on holiday to Spain,
5. [ ] She sometimes plays the guitar in a band,
6. [ ] She doesn't often go out during the week,

a. but she hates game shows.
b. but she's staying in London this summer.
c. ~~but she's reading now and it's midnight!~~
d. but this week she's playing the drums.
e. but she's watching a film at the cinema now.
f. but she doesn't speak Italian.

4 ●● Choose the correct option.

1. We (*usually study*) / *are usually studying* Maths on Mondays, but today *we have* / *we're having* a test.
2. Jenna's listening to music *and* / *but* she's watching TV at the same time! How?
3. I *don't do* / *'m not doing* my homework at the moment because my computer *doesn't work* / *isn't working*.
4. I *wait* / *'m waiting* for my friend, but he is late.
5. *Do you always have* / *Are you always having* a big breakfast before school? No, *I don't* / *I'm not*.
6. My sister *usually wears* / *is usually wearing* jeans, *and* / *but* today she *wears* / *'s wearing* a skirt.

5 ●●● Complete the text with the correct form of the verbs below.

| enjoy | not get | ~~have~~ | hear | love |
| play | practise | sing (x2) | | |

My friend, Liz, is amazing. She's only fifteen, but she [1]<u>has</u> a brilliant weekend job. Every Friday and Saturday night she [2]_____ with a band. She's got a lovely voice. Her brother [3]_____ the guitar. They're both really good musicians. They [4]_____ a lot of money, but they [5]_____ it. The band always [6]_____ in our classroom during the lunch break and I can [7]_____ them now. Mia [8]_____ an Adele song. I [9]_____ their music!

I can talk about what usually happens and what is happening now.

On the Portal
Extra Practice Activities: Lesson 2.4

2.5 Listening and Vocabulary
Describing a friend's personality

1 Write the words for the definitions.
1. This describes someone who only thinks about himself or herself. s<u>e l f i s h</u>
2. This describes someone who is not afraid of new things or challenges. c_ _ _ _ _ _ _ _
3. This describes someone who is not polite. r_ _ _
4. This describes someone who is intelligent. c_ _ _ _ _
5. This describes someone who is always happy. c_ _ _ _ _ _ _

2 Match the adjectives below with pictures A–F.

| bossy | chatty | funny | ~~kind~~ | lazy | polite |

A — _kind_
B — _____
C — _____
D — _____
E — _____
F — _____

3 Choose the correct option.
1. My brother is so (shy) / funny that he has very few friends.
2. Jo is very quiet / friendly and always makes new friends.
3. Carla is rather quiet / chatty. She never says much.
4. Paolo's room is never a mess – he's very tidy / lazy.
5. Mary talks too much! She's never helpful / quiet.

I can understand people talking about their friends.

4 Complete the sentences with adjectives from Exercise 3.
1. Sara doesn't talk very much. She's very _quiet_.
2. Gary's very _____. He's checking my computer at the moment because it isn't working very well.
3. My young sister is quite _____ and she doesn't like meeting new people.
4. I think I'm _____! I can talk about anything!
5. My brother's so _____. He always does things that make me laugh.
6. I'm feeling _____ today. I don't want to do anything.

5 🔊 2.1 Listen to dialogues 1–5 and choose the correct answer.
1. Who is the boy's sister?
   a Anna
   b Sally
   c Alex
2. Where are the speakers?
   a in town
   b in a café
   c in the park
3. When is the girl's party?
   a Wednesday
   b Friday
   c Saturday
4. What is Grace wearing to the concert?
   a dress
   b jeans
   c trainers
5. What is Tim doing?
   a eating his breakfast
   b dancing at a club
   c sleeping in bed

6 🔊 2.1 Listen to the dialogues again. Mark the sentences T (true) or F (false).
1. ☐ The new student is in Class 4.
2. ☐ It isn't raining at the moment.
3. ☐ The boy is giving the girl her birthday present now.
4. ☐ The students are planning to walk to the concert.
5. ☐ Tim stays out late on Fridays.

On the Portal
Extra Practice Activities: Lesson 2.5

2.6 Speaking
Giving and responding to news

1 🔊 2.2 Listen and repeat the phrases.

> **SPEAKING** Giving and responding to news
>
> **Giving news**
> I'm learning (how to speak) Chinese.
> I'm spending a lot of time with my friends/in the art club.
> I'm feeling annoyed because my phone isn't working.
> I'm feeling excited because I'm going to the cinema.
> I'm working on a new project.
> He/She isn't feeling well.
>
> **Responding to news**
> Well done!   Good for you!   Awesome!   Great!   Cool!
> That's terrible!   What a shame!   Poor you!
> No way!   I don't believe it!   You're kidding!

2 Match the sentence halves.
1. [e] I'm learning
2. [ ] I'm spending
3. [ ] My sister isn't feeling
4. [ ] I'm feeling excited
5. [ ] I'm working
6. [ ] I'm feeling very

a   very well. I think she's ill.
b   because it's my birthday next week.
c   tired this morning.
d   on my dance moves at the moment.
e   ~~how to play the piano.~~
f   a lot of time with my cousin.

3 Make sentences from the prompts that give news.
1. my sister / enjoy / her new job
   My sister is enjoying her new job.
2. I / learn / a new language
   _____
3. my mum / not feel well / these days
   _____
4. I / spend a lot of time / at school / at the moment
   _____
5. I'm / work / on / a new story
   _____
6. my dad / feel / worried because he / have problems / with his new car
   _____

4 🔊 2.3 Complete the dialogues with one word in each gap. Then listen and check.

> done   great   kidding   ~~no~~   poor
> shame   that's

1. A: Mateo has stopped his English lessons!
   B: *No* way!
2. A: My Maths results are brilliant!
   B: Well _____!
3. A: My dog's ill.
   B: What a _____!
4. A: This new shirt has got a hole in it.
   B: _____ terrible!
5. A: I've got lots of homework.
   B: _____ you!
6. A: I'm learning Mandarin Chinese!
   B: _____!
7. A: We don't have any classes today!
   B: You're _____!

5 Choose the correct response.
1. I've got free tickets for the concert!
   a What a shame!
   (b) Awesome!
   c Poor you!
2. I can't go to Mike's party.
   a Great!
   b What a shame!
   c Good for you!
3. My dad's got a job in China.
   a Well done!
   b No way!
   c Good for you!
4. They're cutting down those lovely trees in Forest Road.
   a You're kidding!
   b Cool!
   c Poor you!
5. I'm feeling really ill today.
   a Well done!
   b Cool!
   c That's terrible!

Unit 2   22   I can give and respond to news.

2.7 Writing
A semi-formal email

Welcome to eFriends!

Choose one of the people in the profiles and send them an email. This could be the start of a great friendship!

Paulo, 15
Marcia, 14

1 Read the email from Phil to one of the people on the eFriends website and answer the questions.
   1 How many brothers or sisters has he got?
     _____
   2 What instrument does he play? _____
   3 Does he practice with his band every day?
     _____
   4 Does he like his school uniform? _____

Dear Paulo,

I'm writing to tell you about myself and my family.

My name's Phil. I'm fourteen and I have a brother and a sister. My sister's name is Megan and she's twelve. She's really into photography. My brother Adam is nine. They're both nice and funny. Our school is Forest Secondary School. The school day begins at 9 a.m. and finishes at 3.15 p.m. I play the guitar in a band and we practise after school on Wednesdays and at the weekend. Most schools in the UK have a uniform, and we do too. It's uncomfortable and I don't like it! I wear black shoes which are tight and a horrible white shirt! Do you wear a uniform at school? Write and tell me.

I'm looking forward to reading your reply!

Kind regards,
Phil

2 Complete the sentences with one word in each gap.
   1 I'm writing *to* tell you about me and my family.
   2 My friends and _____ usually go to a pizza place after school.
   3 The school day _____ at 8.30 and finishes at 3.00.
   4 I'm looking forward _____ reading about you.
   5 _____ wishes.

3 Complete the table with the words below.

   autumn   March   Monday morning   my birthday
   night   New Year   Sundays   ~~the morning~~   3.15
   the evening   15 November   the weekend   2018

IN	ON	AT
the morning		

WRITING TIME

4 Choose one of the teenagers from the website and write an email to him/her.

1 Find ideas
Make notes about:
* your family and friends.
* a normal school day.
* the clothes students wear in your school.

2 Plan and write
* Organise your ideas into paragraphs. Use Phil's email to help you.
* Write a draft email.

3 Check
* Check language: are the prepositions of time correct?
* Check grammar: are most verbs in the Present Simple and some in the Present Continuous?
* Write a final version of your email.

I can write a semi-formal email.

My Language File

WORDLIST 🔊 2.4

Clothes and accessories

baseball cap (n) _____
belt (n) _____
boots (n) _____
coat (n) _____
dress (n) _____
earrings (n) _____
(fancy-dress) costume (n) _____
glasses (n) _____
gloves (n) _____
handbag (n) _____
hat (n) _____
hoodie (n) _____
jacket (n) _____
jeans (n) _____
necklace (n) _____
scarf (n) _____
shirt (n) _____
shoes (n) _____
shorts (n) _____
sweater (n) _____
top (n) _____
tracksuit (n) _____
trainers (n) _____
trousers (n) _____
T-shirt (n) _____
underwear (n) _____
uniform (n) _____

Adjectives to describe clothes and accessories

baggy (adj) _____
checked (adj) _____
cotton (adj) _____
dark (adj) _____
leather (adj) _____
light (adj) _____
plain (adj) _____
striped (adj) _____
tight (adj) _____
woolly (adj) _____

Adjectives with -ed/-ing

annoyed (adj) _____
annoying (adj) _____
bored (adj) _____
boring (adj) _____
embarrassed (adj) _____
embarrassing (adj) _____
excited (adj) _____
exciting (adj) _____
frightened (adj) _____
frightening (adj) _____
interested (adj) _____
interesting (adj) _____
relaxed (adj) _____
relaxing (adj) _____
tired (adj) _____
tiring (adj) _____

Personality adjectives

bossy (adj) _____
chatty (adj) _____
cheerful (adj) _____
clever (adj) _____
confident (adj) _____
friendly (adj) _____
funny (adj) _____
helpful (adj) _____
kind (adj) _____
lazy (adj) _____
polite (adj) _____
quiet (adj) _____
rude (adj) _____
selfish (adj) _____
shy (adj) _____
tidy (adj) _____

Extra words

beard (n) _____
bracelet (n) _____
celebrate (v) _____
change clothes _____
feel (v) _____
festival (n) _____
footwear (n) _____
get fit _____
have a meal _____
have fun _____
hobby (n) _____
indoors (adv) _____
jewellery (n) _____
laces (n) _____
look cool _____
outdoors (adv) _____
outgoing (adj) _____
party (n) _____
person (n) _____
pocket (n) _____
protect from (v) _____
shopping trip (n) _____
snow boots (n) _____
socks (n) _____
spend time _____
style (n) _____
summer (n) _____
sunglasses (n) _____
walk a dog _____
wear (v) _____
wedding (n) _____
winter (n) _____

Sounds good!

What's up? _____
How's life? _____
How's it going? _____

MY LANGUAGE NOTES

My favourite words/expressions from this unit

Self-check

Vocabulary

1 Complete the sentences with the words below.

> belt   cotton   earrings   scarf
> shorts   trainers   uniform

1 I wear a _____ to school – it's blue.
2 I wear my leather _____ when I play tennis.
3 I like your _____. They really make your ears look nice.
4 Helen usually wears _____ T-shirts in the summer.
5 I need a tight _____ for these jeans.
6 When it's cold, my brother wears a red woolly _____.
7 It's a lovely day today, so I'm wearing my _____.

2 Choose the correct option.
1 My little brother often breaks my things. It's so *annoying / annoyed*.
2 I'm really *tiring / tired* after that long walk.
3 I don't like that film. I really think it's *boring / bored*.
4 This book is really *interesting / interested*. I can't put it down!
5 Angela was so *embarrassing / embarrassed* when her dad came into school.
6 The children are *exciting / excited* about their trip to the zoo tomorrow.
7 I like listening to podcasts when I go to sleep. It's very *relaxing / relaxed*.

3 Complete the sentences.
1 My sister always cleans up. She's very t_____.
2 Maria talks too much. She is very c_____.
3 Becky always helps people. She's k_____.
4 Tom always gets the highest marks in class. He's very c_____.
5 Nick never says hello to anyone! He's very r_____.
6 Mary says everybody what to do. She is very b_____.

Grammar

4 Complete the sentences with the Present Continuous form of the verbs in brackets.
1 Jacky _____ (wear) a blue skirt today.
2 Where _____ (Mike/go)?
3 I _____ (not do) exercise 3 at the moment.
4 _____ (Dan/drive) his dad's car?
5 John _____ (not work). He _____ (sleep).
6 Jen _____ (sit) next to Bill today.
7 Fran _____ (not eat) fruit for lunch.

5 Choose the correct option.

Hi Eva,

What ¹*are you doing / do you do*? I'm sure you're reading a book. You ²*are reading / read* every day! I'm in my room. ³*I'm trying / I try* to choose a dress for the party tonight. ⁴*I'm not wanting / I don't want* to wear the red one. ⁵*I'm always wearing / I always wear* that one to parties. I need new clothes! ⁶*Are you going / Do you go* shopping this Saturday? We can go together. Anyway, I ⁷*do / am doing* a quiz on fashion now. It's fun!

Talk later!
Jess

Speaking

6 Choose the correct response.
1 I'm doing well at school.
   a Good for you!   b What a shame!
2 My computer isn't working.
   a Great!   b Poor you!
3 We've got a lovely new dog.
   a Awesome!   b That's terrible!
4 It's raining again.
   a You're kidding!   b Well done!
5 I've got an expensive new laptop!
   a What a shame!   b No way!

YOUR SCORE

Vocabulary: __/20   Speaking: __/5
Grammar: __/15   Total: __/40

Animal life

VOCABULARY
Animals | Animal body parts | Personality | Looking after pets

GRAMMAR
Past Simple: was/were | Past Simple: regular and irregular verbs

3.1 Vocabulary
Animals

1 ● Complete the names of the animals.
1. sh _a_ _r_ k
2. bu __ __ __ __ __ y
3. ladyb __ __ d
4. g __ __ t
5. ka __ __ __ __ o
6. sn __ __ e
7. tor __ __ se
8. le __ __ __ __

2 ● Choose the correct option.
1. My parents gave me a pet (tortoise)/ gorilla for my birthday.
2. *Polar bears / Owls* live in the Arctic where it's very cold.
3. My friend has a very cute pet *shark / rabbit* which lives in her garden.
4. I have a *cow / horse* which I ride every weekend.
5. Aw, your *donkey / guinea pig* is so small and cute!
6. *Bees / Ants* can beat their wings very fast.

3 ● Decide if the animals below are insects (I), farm animals (F) or wild animals (W).

1. [W] snake
2. [ ] bear
3. [ ] ladybird
4. [ ] goat
5. [ ] leopard
6. [ ] donkey
7. [ ] horse
8. [ ] chicken
9. [ ] ant
10. [ ] owl
11. [ ] cow
12. [ ] bee
13. [ ] kangaroo
14. [ ] gorilla
15. [ ] butterfly

4 ●● Match descriptions 1–8 with photos A–H in Exercise 5.
1. [F] It's very slow.
2. [ ] It lives in the jungle.
3. [ ] It is black and tiny.
4. [ ] It is grey or brown.
5. [ ] It has brown feathers.
6. [ ] It is black and white.
7. [ ] It has big wings.
8. [ ] It has very long ears.

5 Write the names of the animals described in Exercise 4.

A

B

C

D

E

F

G

H

6 ● **Choose the correct answer.**
1 Which animal doesn't have a tail?
   (a) butterfly   b rabbit   c horse
2 Which animal doesn't have fur?
   a snake   b gorilla   c tiger
3 Which animal doesn't have wings?
   a bee   b donkey   c owl
4 Which animal doesn't have feathers?
   a chicken   b owl   c goat
5 Which animal doesn't have claws?
   a leopard   b cow   c polar bear

7 ●● **Complete the sentences with the words below.**

beak   claws   ~~feathers~~   fur   paws
tails   wings

1 Some birds have brightly coloured *feathers*.
2 Dogs move their _____ very fast when they're happy.
3 Bears have different coloured _____. Sometimes it's brown, sometimes white and sometimes black.
4 Ducks have a _____ which they use to eat with.
5 Our dog has long _____ and we have to cut them from time to time.
6 The _____ of a butterfly are usually very pretty.
7 Cats walk quietly on their _____.

8 ●● **Choose the correct option.**
1 A bee *swims* / (*flies*) and has (*wings*) / *claws*.
2 A duck *climbs* / *swims* and has *claws* / *feathers*.
3 A cat *climbs* / *flies* and has *feathers* / *a tail*.
4 A tiger eats *vegetables* / *meat* and has long *wings* / *claws*.
5 A rabbit *jumps* / *swims* and has *feathers* / *fur*.
6 A shark *walks* / *bites* and has sharp *claws* / *teeth*.

I can talk about animals.

9 ●●● **Complete the email with the words below.**

~~butterflies~~   chickens   claws   goats
rabbits   tails   tortoise   wings

Hi Emma
When you're on holiday in Lyndhurst you must visit the Wildlife Centre. It's brilliant. They have a special room for beautiful ¹*butterflies*. They have very pretty ² _____ and there are hundreds of them flying all over the place. Sometimes they land on your arm or head! If you have your little sister with you, she can go to the pets' farm. They usually have some baby animals there. She can pick up the baby ³ _____ – their mothers are out in the field eating grass! And there are a lot of ⁴ _____ with their little round white fluffy ⁵ _____. She can pick them up, but be careful because their ⁶ _____ can be quite sharp! If you want a new pet, you can buy one to take home! The centre also sells their wooden houses to keep in the garden. The ⁷ _____ are really cute too. They lay eggs and make a lot of noise! And there's a ⁸ _____ that is nearly a hundred years old at the centre too! It lives in a warm box in the winter, but in the summer you can see it walking very, very slowly across the grass!

Have fun!
Chris

On the Portal
Extra Practice Activities: Lesson 3.1

3.2 Grammar

Past Simple: was/were

GRAMMAR — Past Simple: was/were

+	I **was** out. She **was** excited. We **were** at the zoo.	
−	I **wasn't** at the shops. She **wasn't** shocked. We **weren't** at home.	
?	**Were** you at the shops? **Was** it fun? **Were** they excited?	Yes, I **was**./No, I **wasn't**. Yes, it **was**./No, it **wasn't**. Yes, we **were**./No, we **weren't**.
	Where **were** you?	
+	there is/are → there **was/were**	
−	there isn't/aren't → there **wasn't/weren't**	

Time expressions: last night/weekend, yesterday, this morning, two days ago, at ten o'clock

1 ● Complete the text with *was*, *wasn't*, *were* and *weren't*.

I ¹*wasn't* at school last week because I ² _____ on holiday with my parents. We ³ _____ in Spain, on the south coast. We ⁴ _____ in a very expensive hotel because Dad wanted a cheap holiday! But it ⁵ _____ nice and there ⁶ _____ a lot of teenagers there – cool for me! Our hotel ⁷ _____ on the beach and I ⁸ _____ in the water every day! It ⁹ _____ very hot, but the sea ¹⁰ _____ quite warm and good for swimming. There ¹¹ _____ an aquarium near the hotel and there ¹² _____ some interesting animals! There ¹³ _____ any sharks or dolphins – just small fish.

2 ● Order the words in brackets to complete the questions.

1 *Were you tired* (tired/you/were) after football yesterday?
2 _____ (your/were/friends) at the party?
3 _____ (Marie/was/class/in) this morning?
4 _____ (shops/were/the) open yesterday evening?
5 _____ (the/was/film) interesting?
6 _____ (was/at/Tim/your) house last night?

3 ● Complete the short answers to the questions in Exercise 2.

1 Yes, *I was*.   4 Yes, _____.
2 No, _____.   5 No, _____.
3 Yes, _____.   6 Yes, _____.

4 ● Choose the correct option.

1 I was (in)/ at the park this morning.
2 We were in / at the cinema last weekend.
3 I was at / in home this morning.
4 Were you at / in Rob's party?
5 They weren't in / at the classroom this morning. It was empty.
6 Was she at / in the concert with you?

5 ●● Complete the dialogue with the correct words.

A: Hi! ¹*Where* were you after school? You ² _____ at the café.
B: No, I ³ _____. I was ⁴ _____ the park with my dog. The weather ⁵ _____ lovely. There ⁶ _____ a lot of rabbits and she was very happy! ⁷ _____ Mark ⁸ _____ the café?
A: Yes, he ⁹ _____. He was with Sally from Class 5. Later they ¹⁰ _____ at the cinema together too! I was there with Jenny.
B: What ¹¹ _____ the film about?
A: It was an adventure film, *Race Against Time*.
B: Ahhh! ¹² _____ it good?
A: It ¹³ _____ very good. I loved it!

6 ●●● Complete the questions.

1 When *were* you in Switzerland? Last week.
2 Where _____ they at lunchtime? In the park.
3 Who _____ you with after school? I was with Jane.
4 What _____ the weather like in Italy? Very hot.
5 What time _____ the film on TV? 7.30.
6 Who _____ on the phone? Carl.

Unit 3 — 28 — I can use *was* and *were* to talk about the past.

On the Portal
Extra Practice Activities: Lesson 3.2

3.3 Reading and Vocabulary

Animals and their personality

1 Read the blog post quickly. Write the names of the animals in photos A–C.

A surprising day at the wildlife centre

Last weekend I was at Oaktree Wildlife centre with my family for a day out. It was brilliant! There were lots of animals, but these were my three favourites. First there were lots of different monkeys. All of them were really playful and adventurous, but my favourites were the mandrills. Did you know that monkeys don't eat bananas in the wild? Lots of people think they do, but they never really find bananas like we have in the supermarkets anywhere. These animals eat other fruit and leaves, flowers, nuts and insects.

Next was the reptiles. My favourite was the chameleon. People often think chameleons change their colour to match their surroundings. For example, they're brown on the ground and green in a tree.

But this isn't true. They actually change colour because of their mood. So, if they feel lively, they change to one colour, and if they feel sad they change to another colour. I really like them whatever their colour!

There was also an aquarium at the wildlife centre, and my favourite animal was there – a blue whale! A lot of people think whales are always friendly, but they can sometimes be aggressive. Whales, like humans have different personalities. Usually they are very sociable animals, though.

- What's your favourite animal?
- Do you know any interesting facts about it?
- Tell me in the comments section below.

2 Read the text again and choose the correct answer.
1. What does the writer learn about monkeys?
   a They never eat bananas.
   b They don't eat bananas in the wild.
   c They don't like bananas.
2. Why do chameleons change colour?
   a Because of their mood.
   b To match their surroundings.
   c Nobody knows.
3. What is the truth about blue whales?
   a They're aggressive to humans.
   b They're always sociable.
   c They have different personalities.

3 Match the highlighted words in the text with the definitions.
1. Someone who has lots of energy and is very active. _____
2. Someone who is very happy and active and wants to have fun. _____
3. Not frightened of trying new things. _____
4. Someone who is friendly and likes being with other people. _____
5. Someone who is angry and/or dangerous. _____

I can understand a blog about a wildlife centre.

3.4 Grammar

Past Simple: regular and irregular verbs

GRAMMAR — Past Simple: regular and irregular verbs

	Regular verbs	Irregular verbs
+	I wanted a bearded dragon.	I went to the kitchen.
–	He didn't want Rex.	She didn't go home.
?	Did she want a pet? Yes, she did./No, she didn't.	Did she go to the kitchen? Yes, she did./No, she didn't.
	What did Mateo want?	Why did he do that?

Past Simple verbs are irregular in the affirmative form only.

1 ● Complete the sentences with the past form of the verbs below.

find   help   look   walk   ~~want~~   write

1. Olly *wanted* to be a vet when he was younger.
2. Jack _____ me with my animal project last night.
3. We _____ at some beautiful photos of Annie's pet cat at break this morning.
4. I _____ your dog in my garden this morning.
5. Megan and Bree _____ a letter to the Queen.
6. The penguins at the zoo _____ in a funny way!

2 ● Complete the sentences with the negative form of the verbs.

1. I needed some paper. I *didn't need* a pen.
2. Harry found his book. He _____ yours.
3. We studied vocabulary. We _____ grammar.
4. They went to the beach. They _____ to the park.
5. I saw Jenna at the party. I _____ Karl.

3 ● Order the words in brackets to complete the questions. Then write short answers.

1. *Did he phone* (did/phone/he) you yesterday?
   Yes, *he did*.
2. _____ (answer/you/did) the teacher's question?
   No, _____.
3. _____ (walk/they/did) to the party?
   No, _____.
4. _____ (like/did/you) my pet guinea pig?
   Yes, _____.
5. _____ (police/did/look/the) for the dog?
   No, _____.

4 ●● Complete the dialogues with the correct Past Simple form of the verbs.

1. (watch)
   A: *Did you watch* the documentary about wild animals last night?
   B: No, I *didn't watch* the documentary, but I *watched* a game show.
2. (phone)
   A: When _____ Hannah?
   B: I _____ her at 7.30, but she wasn't at home.
3. (listen)
   A: _____ to Beyoncè's new song?
   B: Yes, I _____ to it last night. It was brilliant.
4. (see)
   A: _____ Helena last night?
   B: Yes! I _____ her at the party.
5. (draw)
   A: _____ the artist _____ a picture of the mountains?
   B: No. He _____ a picture of some flowers.

5 ●●● Complete the dialogue with the correct form of the verbs below.

~~ask~~   change   decide   not finish
go   not go   look   find   promise

A: Did you start the animal project last night?
B: Yes, I did. I [1] *asked* Andy to help me.
A: But he [2] _____ to the cinema last night.
B: He [3] _____ his plans. He [4] _____ to the cinema. He [5] _____ to help me instead!
A: That was very kind of him!
B: I know. We [6] _____ online and [7] _____ some interesting articles about wildlife in Africa. We [8] _____, but he [9] _____ to help me again tonight.
A: Lucky you!

I can use the Past Simple to talk about past events.

On the Portal
Extra Practice Activities: Lesson 3.4

3.5 Listening and Vocabulary
Looking after pets

1 **WORD FRIENDS** Match the sentence halves.

1 [d] I spend time with
2 [ ] How often do you brush
3 [ ] I have to put fresh
4 [ ] When do you usually take
5 [ ] I feed
6 [ ] We want to train
7 [ ] Where do you

a my cat in the morning. He's always very hungry!
b your dog for a walk?
c my dog to do tricks, but he never does them!
d ~~my cat every day. We play together.~~
e your dog's fur?
f buy food for your dog?
g water in my dog's bowl twice a day.

2 Match sentences 1–7 from Exercise 1 with pictures A–G.

A [ ]

B [ ]

C [ ]

D [ ]

E [1]

F [ ]

G [ ]

I can understand a conversation about pets.

3 🔊 3.1 Listen to five short dialogues. Match dialogues 1–5 with pictures A–E.

A [ ]

B [ ]

C [ ]

D [ ]

E [ ]

4 🔊 3.1 Listen again and choose the correct answer.

1 What does Harry the dog usually eat?
   a dog biscuits
   b the same food as the family
   c chicken
2 What's the weather like?
   a It's raining.   b It's cold.   c It's sunny.
3 How many lions were there when the girl was at the park?
   a none   b two   c four
4 What did the girl NOT do?
   a give cat food to the cat
   b give food to the cat
   c put water in the cat's bowl
5 What is Gran's new pet?
   a a cat   b a tortoise   c a parrot

On the Portal
Extra Practice Activities: Lesson 3.5

3.6 Speaking
Apologising and responding to apologies

1 🔊 **3.2** Listen and repeat the phrases.

SPEAKING	Apologising and responding to apologies
Apologising	**Responding to apologies**
I'm (really/so) sorry.	Never mind.
I didn't mean to do that/it.	No problem.
I feel terrible.	Don't worry.
	Honestly!
	That's all right.
	Just be more careful.

2 Complete the table with the phrases below.

> Don't worry. Honestly! I didn't mean to do that.
> I feel terrible. ~~I'm (really/so) sorry.~~ Just be more careful.
> Never mind. No problem.

Apologising	Responding to apologies
I'm (really/so) sorry.	

3 Choose the correct response.

1 I'm sorry I'm late.
  a I didn't mean to do that.
  b I feel terrible.
  (c) No problem.

2 I'm sorry – I dropped your book in the bath.
  a I feel terrible.
  b It's all my fault.
  c Never mind.

3 I'm sorry I didn't remember to bring your DVD.
  a No problem.
  b I feel terrible.
  c Just be more careful.

4 I'm sorry I knocked your cup off the table.
  a I didn't mean to do that.
  b I'm sorry.
  c Don't worry.

5 I'm sorry I burned the dinner.
  a I'm really sorry.
  b Just be more careful.
  c I feel terrible.

4 🔊 **3.3** Complete the dialogues with one word in each gap. Listen and check.

1 A: I'm *sorry*. I've got tickets for the wrong concert. I feel terrible.
  B: _____! They were really expensive!

2 A: I'm sorry. I didn't finish my homework last night.
  B: _____ mind. You can give it in tomorrow.

3 A: I'm really late for the meeting. I'm really _____.
  B: No _____. Jane's not here yet.

4 A: I'm sorry, but I have to leave early. I need to go to the dentist.
  B: Don't _____, it's fine.

5 A: Oops! I deleted your file. Sorry, I didn't _____ to do that.
  B: Really? Now I've got to write it all again! Just be more _____ next time.

6 A: I'm really sorry. I showed Tommy a photo of you and your French friend in the summer. I feel _____.
  B: That's all _____.

I can make and respond to apologies.

On the Portal
Extra Practice Activities: Lesson 3.6

3.7 Writing
A blog entry

1 Read the blog and answer the questions.
1 Where was Jamie? _____
2 Who was he with? _____
3 How did he feel in the morning? _____

My dolphin adventure by Jamie Harper

Two years ago I ¹*went* (go) on holiday to Florida with my family.

One day, we ² _____ (visit) a dolphin centre. I ³ _____ (be) very excited in the morning because it was my dream to see dolphins.

When we ⁴ _____ (arrive), one of the trainers ⁵ _____ (speak) to our group. They ⁶ _____ (tell) us all about dolphins. We went to meet the dolphins, but at first they ⁷ _____ (not be) there, so I felt sad.

After a short while, the dolphins ⁸ _____ (swim) into the lagoon and I ⁹ _____ (take) photos of them. When we ¹⁰ _____ (meet) the dolphins close, some people were a bit scared, but I wasn't. They ¹¹ _____ (not look) aggressive but beautiful! One swam next to me. We ¹² _____ (have) an amazing time.

It was the best experience ever!

2 Complete the blog with the Past Simple form of the verbs in brackets.

3 Match 1–4 with a–d.
1 [b] Two years   a photos.
2 [ ] I was   b ~~ago~~...
3 [ ] I took   c amazing time.
4 [ ] We had an   d very excited.

4 Match the items in Exercise 3 to functions a–c. One function has two items.
a Describe what happened and how you felt. 2 / __
b Say when the situation/event happened. __
c Say what you think about the situation/event. __

5 Choose the correct option.
1 We saw monkeys (and)/ or tigers at the safari park.
2 I went to Orlando *so / because* I wanted to see the dolphins.
3 I like cats, *or / but* I don't like dogs.
4 The park didn't have dolphins *so / or* sharks.
5 We didn't see any wild animals, *so / because* I felt sad.

WRITING TIME

6 Write a blog entry about a special trip you made. Try to include an animal in your blog.

1 Find ideas
Make notes about:
- where you were.
- who you were with.
- what happened.

2 Plan and write
- Organise your ideas into paragraphs. Use the text in Exercise 1 to help you.
- Write a draft blog entry.

3 Check
- Check language: are the linking words (*and, or, so, but, because*) correct?
- Check grammar: did you use a variety of verbs in the Past Simple?
- Write the final version of your blog entry.

I can write a blog entry.

My Language File

WORDLIST 🔊 3.4

Animals
- ant (n) _____
- bee (n) _____
- butterfly (n) _____
- chicken (n) _____
- cow (n) _____
- donkey (n) _____
- goat (n) _____
- gorilla (n) _____
- guinea pig (n) _____
- horse (n) _____
- kangaroo (n) _____
- ladybird (n) _____
- leopard (n) _____
- owl (n) _____
- parrot (n) _____
- polar bear (n) _____
- rabbit (n) _____
- shark (n) _____
- snake (n) _____
- tortoise (n) _____

Animal body parts
- beak (n) _____
- claw (n) _____
- feather (n) _____
- fur (n) _____
- paw (n) _____
- tail (n) _____
- wing (n) _____

Personality
- adventurous (adj) _____
- aggressive (adj) _____
- lively (adj) _____
- playful (adj) _____
- sociable (adj) _____

Word friends (looking after pets)
- brush his/her fur _____
- buy food for him/her _____
- feed him/her _____
- put fresh water in his/her bowl _____
- spend time with him/her _____
- take him/her for a walk _____
- train him/her _____

Extra words
- animal charity (n) _____
- aquarium (n) _____
- be frightened of _____
- bedding (n) _____
- behaviour (n) _____
- brown bear (n) _____
- cage (n) _____
- cat (n) _____
- catch (v) _____
- clean (v) _____
- colourful (adj) _____
- cute (adj) _____
- dangerous (adj) _____
- elephant (n) _____
- farm animal (n) _____
- food bowl (n) _____
- giraffe (n) _____
- hamster (n) _____
- insect (n) _____
- kitten (n) _____
- live (v) _____
- live animal (n) _____
- lizard (n) _____
- look after a pet _____
- lovable (adj) _____
- monkey (n) _____
- penguin (n) _____
- pet (n) _____
- pick up (v) _____
- play with a pet _____
- raccoon (n) _____
- rescue centre (n) _____
- safari (n) _____
- scratch the furniture _____
- sharp (adj) _____
- skin (n) _____
- sloth (n) _____
- spider monkey (n) _____
- stripe (n) _____
- teeth (n) _____
- tiger (n) _____
- toe (n) _____
- toucan (n) _____
- vet (n) _____
- volunteer (n) _____
- wild animal (n) _____
- work with animals _____
- zebra (n) _____
- zoo (n) _____

Sounds good!
- Good call. _____
- Mind out! _____
- What a mess! _____

MY LANGUAGE NOTES

My favourite words/expressions from this unit

Self-check

Vocabulary

1 Choose the odd one out.
1 **Insects:** ant   snake   bee
2 **Farm animals:** cow   donkey   polar bear
3 **Land animals:** horse   tortoise   shark
4 **Large animals:** horse   chicken   gorilla
5 **Flying animals:** butterfly   rabbit   ladybird
6 **Animal skin:** fur   feather   claw
7 **Animal body parts:** fur   paw   tail
8 **Animal personalities:** lively   playful   feathers

2 Complete the sentences with the words below.

> adventurous   aggressive   lively
> playful   sociable

1 Someone who likes to fight and shout is _____.
2 Someone who likes talking and meeting people is _____.
3 Someone who is active and likes playing is _____.
4 Someone who likes trying new things is _____.
5 Someone who has a lot of energy and does lots of things is _____.

3 Choose the correct option.
1 I need to *buy / have* food for my dog.
2 I *take / brush* my dog's fur every day.
3 My brother's job is to *take / put* fresh water in our dog's bowl in the morning.
4 It's your turn to *feed / food* the cat.
5 You need to *train / feed* your dog not to sit on the sofa.
6 How often do you *go / take* your dog for a walk?
7 How much time do you *take / spend* with your pet every day?

Grammar

4 Make questions (?), affirmative (✓) and negative (✗) sentences with the Past Simple form of *to be*.
1 ✓ I _____ in bed early last night.
2 ? _____ your parents at the concert on Saturday?
3 ✗ That programme _____ very interesting.
4 ? _____ Tom at your party?
5 ? What _____ your favourite film last year?

5 Complete the sentences using the Past Simple form of the verbs in brackets.
1 When I was younger I _____ (not like) classical music.
2 Where _____ (you/go) last night?
3 My dad _____ (not work) last month because he was ill.
4 I phoned you yesterday, but you _____ (not answer).
5 _____ (the teacher/teach) some new grammar in class today?

6 Choose the correct option.
1 I *wasn't / weren't* at home last night.
2 Why *wasn't / weren't* Chloe at school today?
3 *Do / Did* Michaela go to the cinema yesterday?
4 My parents *weren't / didn't* have a pet when they were young.
5 We *stay / stayed* at home last night.

Speaking

7 Complete the dialogues with the words below.

> feel   mean   mind   no   so

1 A: I'm _____ sorry. I didn't _____ to do that.
  B: Never _____, it's OK.
2 A: I _____ terrible.
  B: _____ problem. These things happen.

YOUR SCORE

Vocabulary: __/20   Speaking: __/5
Grammar: __/15   Total: __/40

Reading Time 1

Karen and the Artist

Karen's job takes her to many places. She loves art, and in Rome she sees some beautiful pictures. But the artist can't sell them and he has no money. Can Karen sell his pictures for him?

Karen takes a picture and telephones for a taxi. She takes the taxi to Bond Street and goes into an art gallery. The gallery is small but expensive. A woman is sitting at a table. She is reading a book.

'Hello,' she says.
'Good afternoon,' Karen says. 'I've got a picture here, and I want to sell it.'
'Who's the artist?' The woman doesn't look up.
'Antonio Brunetti,' Karen says. 'He's …
'I'm sorry.' The woman starts to read her book again. 'I don't know that name.'
A man comes into the gallery. 'I've got a new Sherman for you!' he says. 'It's wonderful.'
'Who?' the woman says.
'Oh, you know him,' the man says. 'Sherman! He's got an exhibition at the Galerie Saint Michel in Paris!'
'Oh!' The woman puts down her book. 'Let's see. Yes, I like it. Sherman, you said? I can give you £800.'
Quietly, Karen goes away.
She walks across the street and goes into the Astra Gallery.
'I've got a wonderful new Brunetti for you,' she says to the man. 'Look at this.'
'What?' the man says. 'Who's Brunetti?'
'Oh, you know him,' Karen says. 'He's got an exhibition at the Leonardo in Rome.'
'Oh,' the man says. 'Show me.' He looks at the picture. 'Very good,' he says. 'Brunetti, eh? At the Leonardo? OK. I can give you … £900.'
Karen is very happy, but she doesn't smile.
'Hmm …' she says.
'All right, £1,000,' the man says.
'OK,' Karen says.
The man gives her a cheque for £1,000.
'Thank you,' Karen says.

Before you read

1 Match places 1–4 with photos A–D.

1 study   2 art gallery   3 café   4 airport

A ☐
B ☐
C ☐
D ☐

2 Look at the book cover and read the blurb. What do you think happens in the story?

While you read

3 🔊 RT1.1 Read and listen to the story. Mark the sentences T (true) or F (false).

1 ☐ Karen is an artist.
2 ☐ She travels a lot.
3 ☐ She meets an artist in Rome.
4 ☐ The artist she meets is very successful.
5 ☐ She tries to sell his pictures for him.

4 Read the story again. Number events a–f in the order that they happen.

a ☐ A man brings a picture to the gallery.
b ☐ Karen goes to an art gallery in Bond Street.
c ☐ Karen sells the picture.
d ☐ The woman in the art gallery says she doesn't know the artist.
e ☐ The man sells the picture.
f ☐ Karen goes to the Astra Gallery.

5 Choose the correct answer.

1 The first art gallery is ____.
   a cheap   b beautiful   c expensive
2 The woman in the art gallery thinks the artist is ____.
   a not very good   b famous   c not famous
3 The man in the Astra Gallery ____ Brunetti.
   a doesn't know   b doesn't like   c knows
4 He buys the picture for ____.
   a £900   b £1,000   c £800

After you read

6 Complete the sentences with the prepositions below.

across   at   away   down   into   up

1 She said 'hello' to me, but didn't look _____.
2 A man came _____ the art gallery.
3 Karen walked _____ the road to another art gallery.
4 The man looked _____ the picture.
5 The woman put _____ the book on the table.
6 Karen went _____ and left the gallery.

7 Look at the text and write the adjectives for the definitions.

1 another word for fantastic: w_____
2 the opposite of sad: h_____
3 not very big: s_____
4 when something costs too much: e_____
5 very pretty: b_____

8 **WRAP UP** Complete the information about the story.

Title: _____
Type: *crime story / love story / adventure story*
Main characters: _____
_____
Important object: _____
My opinion: ☆☆☆☆☆

Cool tech!

VOCABULARY
Digital devices | Using technology |
Computer equipment | Phrasal verbs |
Favourite websites | Computer problems

GRAMMAR
Used to | Verb patterns

4   4.1   Vocabulary
Technology

1 ● Complete the words.
1 B _l_ _u_ _e_ to _o_ _t_ _h_® s _p_ _e_ _a_ ker
2 ___ ___ i ___ l c ___ ___ r ___
3 ___ i ___ s ___ ___ b ___ ___ ___
4 ___ ___ e ___ ___ so ___ ___
5 h ___ ___ s ___ ___ ___ ___ d ___ t
6 ___ ___ ___ ___ e ch ___ ___ ___
7 ___ a ___ ph ___ ___ ___
8 s ___ ___ ___ w ___ ___

2 ● Match words from Exercise 1 with photos 1–8.

1 _digital camera_    2 _____

3  _____   4 _____

5  _____   6 _____

7  _____   8 _____

3 ●● Complete the sentences with words from Exercise 1.
1 My best present ever was a _games console_. It was very expensive, but I play on it a lot with my friends.
2 Has anyone seen my _____? My phone's dead.
3 I use my _____ to talk to my friends everywhere I go. I've got a cool ringtone too.
4 My aunt uses her _____ to track her exercise when she goes running.
5 I love my _____. Who needs cables any more?
6 Let's get the _____, so we can listen to music in the garden.
7 My brother takes lots of photos and my dad got him a brilliant _____ for his birthday.

4 ● **WORD FRIENDS** Complete the words in the sentences.
1 I l _i_ _s_ _t_ _e_ _n_ to podcasts with my wireless earbuds.
2 I l___k for information on my smartphone.
3 I t_____ photos with my digital camera.
4 I d_____ apps to my smartphone all the time.
5 I p___n__ friends with my smartphone.
6 I c___c__ social media on my laptop.
7 I m_____ video clips on my smartphone.
8 I p_a__ online games on my games console.
9 I c_____g__ my phone with my phone charger.
10 I c_____k the time on my smartwatch.
11 I j__i__ an online class on Fridays.
12 I s____d messages to my friends.

Unit 4   38

5 ●● Match the sentence halves.

1. [h] I always listen
2. [ ] We're joining
3. [ ] My friend checks
4. [ ] My dad ususally checks
5. [ ] I like sending
6. [ ] My mum always forgets to charge
7. [ ] My friends and I like
8. [ ] I need to search

a an online cooking class tomorrow.
b the internet to find some information for my homework.
c emails in class and the teacher gets angry with her.
d watching video clips online.
e the time on his smartphone.
f texts because it's quick.
g her phone and can't use it.
h ~~to podcasts when I'm on the bus.~~

6 ● Complete the sentences with the words below.

keyboard   memory   printer   scanner
~~screen~~   touchscreen   USB cable

1. I need to get a new *screen* for my phone, it's broken.
2. I can't type the letter 'E' on my _____ anymore!
3. I'll use the _____ to make digital copies then email them to you.
4. My old computer doesn't have much _____, so it's really slow.
5. It's much easier to use a _____ than a traditional keyboard and mouse.
6. Oh no, the _____'s broken. Everything comes out blue.
7. I can't find the _____ to connect my phone to my computer.

7 ●● Choose the correct answer.

1. My friend is making a video ___ of her dog to post online.
   a screen   (b) clip   c app
2. Please check your ___. I'm sure I sent you the email.
   a keyboard   b screen   c phone
3. My ___ headset isn't working; it won't charge.
   a handsfree   b digital   c memory
4. Why can I never find a USB ___ when I need one?
   a console   b headset   c cable
5. You wear your ___ all day and it gives you information about how much exercise you did.
   a earphones   b camera   c smartwatch
6. How often do you ___ friends with your smartphone?
   a search   b phone   c watch

8 ●●● Complete the blog with one word in each gap.

I guess I'M A COMPUTER FREAK!

I'm always on my computer and I love my gadgets! When I wake up I ^{1}*check* social media and texts. While I'm having breakfast, I ^{2}_____ to podcasts on my Bluetooth® speaker and send some messages to my best friend. I don't often phone her because it's quicker and easier to talk via messages! I have my ^{3}_____ in my pocket with me everywhere – even in class. I can go online and ^{4}_____ for information – that's educational! At break and after school I ^{5}_____ games on my phone and then in the evening I sometimes use the games ^{6}_____ and play more games online. I wear a ^{7}_____ all day, so in the evening I look at it and see how much exercise I did. At the end of the day my phone battery is down, but it always takes me ages to find a phone ^{8}_____!

I can talk about technology.

4.2 Grammar
Used to

> **GRAMMAR** — Used to
>
> We use *used to* to talk about habits and states that were true in the past, but are not true anymore.
>
> | + | We **used to talk** when you came to visit. |
> |---|---|
> | – | We **didn't use to have** phones. |
> | ? | **Did** you **use to send** postcards? / Yes, we **did**. No, we **didn't**. |
> | | How **did** you **use to communicate**? |

1 ● Choose the correct option.
1. When she was young, my mum (**used**) / use to write letters.
2. She didn't *used / use* to send emails.
3. Did you *used / use* to play online games when you were younger?
4. I used to *go / went* to the cinema every week when I lived in the city.
5. A: Did you use to have a digital camera?
   B: Yes, I *used to / did*.
6. My dad didn't *use / use to* have a smartphone.

2 ● Complete the sentences with the correct form of *used to* and the verb in brackets.
1. I <u>used to have</u> (have) a really nice tablet, but then I broke it.
2. My gran _____ (not search) the internet, but now she's always on it!
3. My parents _____ (listen) to music in the evenings.
4. _____ (you/take) photos with a digital camera?
5. We _____ (not play) games online.
6. Where _____ (you/go) to school?
7. Jamie _____ (live) in London before he moved here.
8. My dad _____ (not download) apps on his smartphone.
9. What books _____ (you/read) when you were younger?
10. My cousins _____ (share) videos of their pets.

3 ●● Write questions for the answers.
1. A: <u>Did you use to have</u> a smartwatch?
   B: No, I didn't use to have a smartwatch.
2. A: What time _____ to bed?
   B: I used to go to bed at 8 p.m. when I was ten.
3. A: Where _____ ?
   B: I used to live in Manchester.
4. A: Who _____ online games with?
   B: I used to play online games with my friends in Canada.
5. A: When _____ photos?
   B: I used to take photos at the weekend.
6. A: How often _____ to podcasts?
   B: I used to listen to podcasts every day.

4 ●●● Complete the dialogue with the correct form of *used to* and the verbs below.

not communicate	decide	~~do~~	have
meet	not play	spend	stay	talk

A: What ¹<u>did you use to do</u> in your free time when you were young, Mum?
B: Well, we ²_____ online games all day, that's for sure!
A: Neither do we!
B: Ha ha, I know. Well, I ³_____ my friends at a café at the weekend, and then we ⁴_____ what to do after that. Sometimes we went to the cinema, and sometimes we ⁵_____ at the café and hang out with each other, talk about things, you know.
A: What ⁶_____ about?
B: Oh, different things – teachers we liked at school, our plans, things like that. We ⁷_____ online as much as you do these days. I think we saw a lot more of each other in person.
A: Oh, that sounds nice.
B: Yes, it was. We ⁸_____ a lot of fun.
A: ⁹_____ a lot of time with your friends?
B: Yes, I saw them every day!

I can use *used to* to talk about things that were true in the past, but aren't true now.

On the Portal
Extra Practice Activities: Lesson 4.2

4.3 Reading and Vocabulary
Technological innovations

1 Read the introduction to the article. Which of these things can drones deliver?

> clothes   food   furniture   medicine   post

My experience of a drone delivery

Drones are able to deliver lots of different small things, such as food, post, medicine and clothes. I didn't use to use delivery services much, but when I *found out* about this service I decided to *check it out*. Here's what happened.

I needed a new T-shirt, and I never used to order clothes online because you can't *try them on* first. But with this service you can return it easily.

So, I *switched on* my phone, opened the app, and ordered my T-shirt. The app said the delivery would take 45 minutes, and I could track the drone on a map. I followed the drone on the map, but then half way it just stopped. I wasn't sure what was wrong, so I called the company. They said the drone was stuck, so they started it again and said it was fine. After I *hung up*, I checked on the drone and it was moving again.

Then I heard it getting closer, so I went outside, looked up and saw it coming! It landed in my front garden. I entered a code on the back of it from my app, and it said, 'Good morning. Here is your delivery.' Wow! I opened it up and there it was. Then it said, 'Goodbye!' and disappeared again.

The whole experience was amazing, and now I use it all the time.

I can understand a report about new technologies.

2 Read the article and choose the correct answer.
1. Why didn't the writer use to buy clothes online?
   a He didn't want to try them.
   b You couldn't try them on first.
   c They took a long time to arrive.
2. What did the writer do when the drone stopped?
   a He phoned the delivery company.
   b He went and got it.
   c He looked for a map.

3 Read the text again and complete the notes with a word or short phrase.

- How to order: [1]with an *app*
- What he ordered: [2]a _____
- Delivery time: [3]_____ minutes
- Where it landed: [4]_____
- How to open it: with a [5]_____ from the app.

4 **WORD FRIENDS** Complete the sentences with the correct form of the highlighted phrasal verbs in the text.
1. After you *switch on* the computer, it needs about five minutes to be ready to use.
2. You can _____ a lot of information about drones on the internet.
3. There's a new gadget shop in town. I'm going to go and _____ it _____. Would you like to come?
4. I waited for a long time for them to answer the phone, but in the end I just _____ and went out.
5. I love your smartwatch. Can I _____ it _____?

On the Portal
Extra Practice Activities: Lesson 4.3

4.4 Grammar
Verb patterns

> **GRAMMAR** **Verb patterns**
>
> - We use **to + the infinitive** after these verbs:
>   agree, decide, forget, learn, need, remember, try, want, would/'d like.
>   I *try to switch* it *off* sometimes.
> - We use **verb + -ing** after these verbs:
>   can't stand, don't mind, enjoy, finish, hate, keep, like, love, prefer, stop.
>   I *prefer texting* friends.

1 Match the sentence halves.
1. [b] My friend agreed
2. [ ] I enjoy
3. [ ] Carla doesn't mind phoning people, but she prefers
4. [ ] Oh no! I forgot
5. [ ] I'd like

a texting her friends.
b ~~to help me with my homework.~~
c to download this app, but it's too expensive.
d to bring my phone charger!
e talking to them in person.

2 ● Choose the correct option.
1. Please stop *to make* / (*making*) that noise. It's terrible!
2. Did you remember *to charge* / *charging* your tablet?
3. You need *to switch* / *switching* it off and on again.
4. I can't stand *to text* / *texting* people. Talking is much better.
5. Do you want *to see* / *seeing* my new app?
6. Let me just finish *to write* / *writing* this email then I'll help you.

3 ●● Complete the sentences with the correct form of the verb in brackets.
1. My mum enjoys *watching* (watch) films online.
2. I prefer _____ (read) adventure books to _____ (go) to concerts.
3. I sometimes forget _____ (charge) my phone overnight.
4. Jake decided _____ (leave) his phone at home for the day! He went crazy!
5. My gran is learning _____ (use) social media – she's doing well.
6. I can't stand _____ (get) texts on my phone from advertisers.

4 ●●● Choose the correct option.

my BLOG

I love ¹*to go* / (*going*) on social media! Every morning I enjoy ²*to read* / *reading* posts from my friends and ³*to look* / *looking* at the photographs they upload. It's also great for keeping in touch with old friends. If I forget ⁴*to reply* / *replying* to posts or comments, social media reminds me! I also like ⁵*to watch* / *watching* video clips, especially funny ones with animals. Last week I decided ⁶*to make* / *making* a video of my cat. I tried ⁷*to film* / *filming* her in my bedroom, but she kept ⁸*to run* / *running* out of the room! Then the camera stopped ⁹*to work* / *working*. So, I waited until the next day and my brother helped me ¹⁰*to fix* / *fixing* it. It was perfect and I made a video of my cat! I wanted ¹¹*to study* / *studying* film and photography at college, but after yesterday – maybe not! I'd also like a job in programming. I learned ¹²*to design* / *designing* websites last year. That was fun! I also made some websites for my friends.

I can make sentences with verbs followed by *to*-infinitive or the *-ing* form.

4.5 Listening and Vocabulary
Favourite websites

1 **WORD FRIENDS** Complete the sentences with the verbs below.

> chat   click   download   follow
> search   share   upload   view

1 I often *search* the web for information for school projects.
2 I make a lot of videos and I like to _____ them with my friends online.
3 Did you _____ that brilliant video of the eagle at the top of the Burj Khalifa from the link I sent you?
4 I often _____ online with my best friend.
5 _____ on the link in this email and you can see the website I told you about.
6 I often _____ photographs to share with my friends on social media.
7 Who do you _____ on social media?
8 Did anyone _____ our video yesterday?

2 🔊 4.1 Listen to Tom talking to his grandad about a project he did. Complete the notes.

- Tom's project is about the history of ¹*computers*.
- Tom got an ² _____ for it.
- Tom spent ³ _____ on the project.
- Snopes began in ⁴ _____ .
- Today, over twenty ⁵ _____ people visit the website each month.
- Tom's grandad wants some information about a favourite ⁶ _____ .

3 🔊 4.1 Listen again and choose the correct answer.

1 What is Tom's grandad surprised by in Tom's project?
  a the age of the first computer
  b Tom's mark
  c how long it took Tom
2 What do 20 million people do every month?
  a write articles for Wikipedia
  b check articles on Snopes
  c read articles on Snopes
3 Why is Snopes popular today?
  a I's quick.
  b It's correct.
  c It's interesting.
4 Where did Tom's grandad get his information?
  a in newspapers
  b at school
  c at the library
5 People check articles now to be sure that
  a they're correct.
  b they're interesting.
  c they're well written.

4 🔊 4.2 Complete the sentences from the dialogue with the correct prepositions. Then listen and check.

1 Did you spend a long time *on* it?
2 I spent an hour looking for the information and then another two hours typing it _____ .
3 You can look _____ anything!
4 You just type _____ the subject and it's all there in front of you.
5 Can I go on this site to find _____ about a writer that I like?

5 Choose the correct option.

1 I'd like to find on /(out) about some new apps for my tablet.
2 I spent three hours *for / on* my homework last night.
3 Where do I type *on / in* the name of the site?
4 Click *on / up* this link to get to the page about the history of computers.

I can understand a conversation about a popular website.

On the Portal
Extra Practice Activities: Lesson 4.5

4.6 Speaking
Talking about technology problems

1 🔊 4.3 Listen and repeat the phrases.

> **SPEAKING** — Talking about technology problems
>
> You need to switch it off and on again/charge it.
> You need to press Control-Alt-Delete.
> Let me/Let's try (something).
> Look at the FAQs (Frequently Asked Questions) on this website.
> Let's search online (for a solution).
> How about calling the shop?
> Shall we look for a blog or an online forum?

2 Match the sentence halves.

1. [c] Let me try
2. [ ] You need to switch
3. [ ] Look at the
4. [ ] You need
5. [ ] How about
6. [ ] Let's search
7. [ ] Shall we

a FAQs on this website.
b calling Jess?
c ~~that.~~
d look for a blog or an online forum?
e it off and on again.
f online for a solution.
g to charge it.

3 🔊 4.4 Complete the dialogue with phrases from Exercise 2. Then listen and check.

Jamie: There's something wrong with my phone, I think. It's really slow.
Alysha: You need to ¹*charge it*.
Jamie: No, I don't, look. It's at ninety-five percent!
Alysha: Oh, I see. Well, maybe you need to switch it ²_____ again.
Jamie: OK, ³_____ that. Hang on, it takes a few minutes to start again.
Jamie: Seriously? No, it's still slow.
Alysha: I don't know. ⁴_____ calling Jess? She's good with technology.
Jamie: No, she's at her swimming club.
Alysha: OK, let's search online ⁵_____. We might be able to find something.
Jamie: Good idea. ⁶_____ for a blog or an online forum?
Alysha: Yes, something like that might help. Or …
Jamie: Or what?
Alysha: Here we are. Look at the FAQs ⁷_____. It looks like this is a common problem with that phone.
Jamie: Ah, right! What we need to do is …

4 Choose the correct option.

1. I don't need to (charge) / switch it. It's at 95 percent!
2. How *around / about* calling Jess?
3. Let's search online *for / of* a solution.
4. *Shall / Will* we look for a blog or an online forum?
5. Look at the FAQs *in / on* this website.

5 **WORD FRIENDS** Choose the correct answer.

1. My computer ____ this morning and I lost all my work.
   a isn't working   (b) crashed
2. My phone's screen is ____. Nothing is moving!
   a frozen   b died
3. He tried to charge his tablet, but it didn't work. The battery ____.
   a died   b crashed
4. Our internet connection is ____ – it's terrible!
   a frozen   b slow
5. The printer ____ because there's no ink in it.
   a doesn't work   b died

I can talk about technology problems.

On the Portal
Extra Practice Activities: Lesson 4.6

4.7 Writing

A review of an app

GazerStar by Patrick Bird

Today, I'm reviewing a new app called GazerStar. It's a cool new app for looking at the sky.

WHAT IS IT FOR?
It is used for identifying stars in the sky. You can use it to learn about the universe.

GOOD POINTS
The quality of the graphics is very good. It's also good for learning the names of the planets and stars you are looking at. The picture gallery is great for discovering astronomy too.

BAD POINTS
Sometimes it is a bit difficult to navigate. And it isn't easy to find the different features in the app.

DO YOU RECOMMEND IT?
Definitely. I recommend this app for anyone who is interested in space. The fun lasts for ages! You can point your phone at the sky and find out what is happening in space!

---

1 Read the review and answer the questions.
1. What is the app used for?
2. Why should you download it?
3. What does Patrick like about it?
4. What doesn't he like about it?
5. Does he recommend it?

2 Choose the correct option.
1. Today, I'm *writing / (reviewing)* a new app called GazerStar.
2. It's a new app *for / to* looking at the sky.
3. You can use it *for / to* learn about the universe.
4. Sometimes it is a *lot / bit* difficult to navigate.
5. The fun lasts *for / to* ages!

3 Complete the sentences with *for* or *to*.
1. Many people also use it *to* discover new music.
2. This app is used _____ chatting to friends.
3. You can use it _____ send photos.
4. It's ideal _____ editing photos.
5. It's my favourite app _____ reading the news.

WRITING TIME

4 Write a review of a device, gadget, game or app.

1 Find ideas
Make notes for a review.
- What is the product/its name/the price?
- What is it for?
- What are its good/bad points?
- Do you recommend it?

2 Plan and write
- Organise your ideas into paragraphs. Use Patrick's review to help you.
- Write a draft review.

3 Check
- Check language: are the expressions of purpose (*for* + *-ing* and *to* + infinitive) correct?
- Check grammar: are the verb patterns correct?
- Write the final version of your review.

I can write a review of an app.

My Language File

WORDLIST 🔊 4.5

Digital devices
- Bluetooth® speaker (n) _____
- digital camera (n) _____
- games console (n) _____
- handsfree headset (n) _____
- phone charger (n) _____
- smartphone (n) _____
- smartwatch (n) _____
- wireless earbuds (n) _____

Word friends (using technology)
- charge your phone _____
- check social media _____
- check the time _____
- download apps _____
- join an online class _____
- listen to music _____
- listen to podcasts _____
- look for information _____
- make video clips _____
- phone a friend _____
- play online games _____
- send messages _____
- send texts _____
- take photos _____

Computer equipment
- keyboard (n) _____
- memory (n) _____
- microphone (n) _____
- printer (n) _____
- scanner (n) _____
- screen (n) _____
- touchscreen (n) _____
- USB cable (n) _____

Word friends (phrasal verbs)
- check out (v) _____
- find out (v) _____
- hang up (v) _____
- switch on (v) _____
- try on (v) _____

Word friends (favourite websites)
- click on links _____
- chat online _____
- download videos _____
- follow people _____
- search the web _____
- share photos _____
- share videos _____
- upload videos _____
- view videos _____

Word friends (computer problems)
- The battery died. _____
- The computer crashed. _____
- The computer isn't working. _____
- The internet connection is slow. _____
- The mouse doesn't work. _____
- The printer doesn't work. _____
- The screen's frozen. _____

Extra words
- app (n) _____
- be addicted to _____
- buy and sell things _____
- call a helpline _____
- charge (v) _____
- communicate (v) _____
- connect to (v) _____
- desktop computer (n) _____
- device (n) _____
- document (n) _____
- drone (n) _____
- edit videos _____
- electronic (adj) _____
- extra (adj) _____
- fix a problem _____
- gadget (n) _____
- hi-tech (adj) _____
- innovation (n) _____
- install a computer program _____
- keep in touch _____
- laptop (n) _____
- last (v) _____
- offline (adj) _____
- online forum (n) _____
- password (n) _____
- phone battery (n) _____
- phone box (n) _____
- read articles _____
- recommend (v) _____
- save photos _____
- social networking site (n) _____
- sound (n) _____
- stay calm _____
- switch off (v) _____
- tablet (n) _____
- take (regular) breaks _____
- technology (n) _____
- text (v) _____
- waterproof (adj) _____
- website (n) _____
- wi-fi (n) _____

Sounds good!
- Good for you. _____
- Seriously? _____

MY LANGUAGE NOTES

My favourite words/expressions from this unit

Unit 4   46

Self-check

Vocabulary

1 Write the words for the definitions.
1. We play video games on this.
   c _ _ _ _ _ _ _ _
2. Use this to give your phone power.
   c _ _ _ _ _ _ _
3. You use this to make phone calls without using your hands.
   h _ _ _ _ _ _ _   h _ _ _ _ _ _
4. You type on this. k _ _ _ _ _ _ _ _
5. You take photos with this.
   d _ _ _ _ _ _ _   c _ _ _ _ _ _
6. You read or watch things on this.
   s _ _ _ _ _ _
7. Use this to track your exercise.
   s _ _ _ _ _ _ _ _ _ _
8. Use this to connect your phone to your computer via USB. c _ _ _ _

2 Complete the sentences with the words below.

| check | download | listen | make |
| play | search | send | |

1. I _____ my emails every hour.
2. My friend and I _____ online games after school.
3. I sometimes _____ texts to my friends during lessons!
4. Don't _____ too many apps or your phone will become slow.
5. We often _____ video clips and put them online.
6. I always _____ to podcasts in bed. It helps me go to sleep.
7. You might find the answer if you _____ the internet.

3 Choose the correct option.
1. I can't join the online lessons because my internet connection is *frozen / slow*.
2. Let's go and *check / find* out that new computer shop in the centre.
3. So rude! He just *switched / hung* up the phone!
4. *Switch / Hang* off your computer and come and have dinner now.
5. Aren't you going to *check / try* on those shoes before you buy them?

Grammar

4 Complete the sentences with the correct form of *used to* and the verbs in brackets.
1. I _____ (play) a lot of games when I was younger.
2. I _____ (not play) tennis.
3. _____ your teacher _____ (give) you a lot of homework?
4. Tony _____ (write) messages every day!
5. We _____ (not go) to school on Fridays.
6. _____ your friends _____ (visit) you?
7. I _____ (not send) emails to my friends.

5 Complete the sentences with the correct form of the verbs in brackets.
1. I enjoyed _____ (go) to see the film with you.
2. What time did you stop _____ (work) last night?
3. I agreed _____ (go) to the party with Ben.
4. I don't mind _____ (help) you.
5. Jason decided _____ (learn) to drive next year.
6. Don't forget _____ (feed) the cat this evening.
7. I'd like _____ (find) out more about space.
8. I hate _____ (read) books about famous people.

Speaking

6 Complete the dialogue with the words below.

| calling | charge | online | search | switch |

A: Ah, my laptop's crashed.
B: You need to ¹_____ it.
A: No, it's fully charged.
B: OK, well you need to ²_____ it off and on.
A: It still doesn't work. What can I do?
B: How about ³_____ the laptop company?
A: I don't know their number. Let's ⁴_____ online for a solution.
B: Or shall we look for an ⁵_____ forum?

YOUR SCORE

Vocabulary: __/20   Speaking: __/5
Grammar: __/15   Total: __/40

My place, my space

VOCABULARY
Things in the home | Prepositions of place | Housework | Adverbs of manner | Places in town

GRAMMAR
Defining relative clauses | Modal verbs: *can*, *have to* and *must*

5.1 Vocabulary

Things in the home

1 ● Match words 1–8 with photos A–H.
1. *E* armchair
2. ☐ coffee table
3. ☐ iron
4. ☐ roof
5. ☐ dishwasher
6. ☐ sofa
7. ☐ plant
8. ☐ sink

A, B, C, D, E, F, G, H

2 ● Choose the correct option.
1. Put the milk in the *fridge* / *microwave* to keep it fresh, please.
2. I need a bigger *cupboard* / *wardrobe*. I've got too many clothes!
3. My mum has some lovely *curtains* / *rugs* on her windows.
4. I've got a big *mirror* / *bedside table* on my wall which I use when I do my make-up.
5. I always sing when I'm in the *shower* / *wardrobe*. My family hate it!
6. There is some soup in that pan on the *cooker* / *washing machine*. It will be ready soon.

3 ● Choose the odd one out.
1. shower   sink   (wardrobe)   rug
2. cooker   dishwasher   ceiling   microwave
3. light   sofa   mirror   roof
4. rug   vacuum cleaner   fridge   washing machine
5. bedside table   wardrobe   plant   armchair

4 ●● Write the words for the definitions.
1. You usually have a lamp on this.
   b_e_ _d_ _s_ _i_ _d_ _e_ t_a_ _b_ _l_ _e_
2. This is the top of a room. c__ __ __ __ __
3. You put books here. b__ __ __ __ __
4. You come into this when you enter the house. h__ __ __
5. You put this on the floor. r__ __
6. You put things in it. c__ __ __ __ __ __
7. You stand on this. f__ __ __
8. This is a living thing. p__ __ __ __

5 ●● Complete the sentences with the correct words below.

| bedside table   bookcase   cupboard   curtains   light |
| vacuum cleaner   ~~wardrobe~~   washing machine |

1. I need a new *wardrobe* to put all my clothes in.
2. Don't forget to switch off the _____ in your room when you go out.
3. I knocked over the alarm clock that is on my _____.
4. My dog is really scared of the _____. He always hides when we use it to clean the floor.
5. My sister never puts plates and glasses in the _____.
6. I haven't got any clean clothes, but I don't know how to use the _____.
7. I like these new _____ because they cover the windows well.
8. My bother loves reading and he needs a bigger _____ for all his books.

Unit 5 48

6 ● Look at the picture. Complete the sentences with the correct words or phrases below.

above   behind   between   in front of
next to   ~~on~~   opposite   under

1 The cat is lying *on* the rug.
2 The dog is _____ the cat.
3 The pets are _____ the fireplace.
4 The mirror is _____ the two bookcases.
5 A clock is _____ the fireplace.
6 A letter is _____ the clock.
7 My school bag is _____ the coffee table.
8 The coffee table is _____ the sofa.

7 ●● **WORD FRIENDS** Choose the correct answer.
1 It's your turn to ___ the ironing.
  a tidy   (b) do   c make
2 Can you ___ your bed, please?
  a do   b make   c tidy
3 Don't worry, I'll ___ the rubbish.
  a tidy   b put on   c sort
4 I'll wash the dishes if you ___ them.
  a dry   b do   c make
5 You can't go out until you ___ your room.
  a tidy   b take out c make
6 Can you ___ the floor today?
  a vacuum   b make   c do
7 You can ___ the cooking and I'll clean the floor.
  a do   b make   c sort
8 Don't forget to ___ the dishwasher later.
  a take out b do   c put on

I can talk about things in the home and housework.

8 ●● Complete the words in the sentences.
1 Sorry, I was in the s*h o w e r* and I didn't hear the phone.
2 Can you water my plant? It's b_ _ _ _ _ the sofa.
3 Look at this mess! I need to v_ _ _ _ _ the floor.
4 Gran is in her a_ _ _ _ _ _. She's watching TV.
5 My dad often d_ _ _ the cooking in our house.
6 I like a dark bedroom at night, so I always close my c_ _ _ _ _ _.
7 It's your turn to t_ _ _ o_ _ the rubbish in the morning.
8 Can you p_ _ o_ the dishwasher, please?

9 ●●● Complete the email with the correct words.

Hi Bella,

We moved to a new house last week. It's really big. There's a lovely kitchen with a very modern ¹*cooker*. We have a ²_____ – so we don't have to do the washing up. There's a big window above the ³_____, so you can look at the garden while you're cooking! The ⁴_____ room is very big, so we need a bigger ⁵_____ to sit on while we watch TV! I've got a nice bedroom. Mum and Dad bought me a new ⁶_____ to put my lamp on and a nice red ⁷_____ to put on the floor. At the moment the ⁸_____ are green, but I want to get some striped ones. In my room I've got a door which leads to my own ⁹_____ with a shower and toilet! Wonderful!

5.2 Grammar
Defining relative clauses

> **GRAMMAR** — Defining relative clauses
>
> - We use **who** or **that** for people.
>   *She's the woman who lives next door.*
> - We use **which** or **that** for things.
>   *Here are some things which I love about my home.*
>   *There are some things that annoy me.*
> - We use **where** for places.
>   *This is the flat where we live.*

1 ● Choose the correct option.
1. The house *where* / *which* my friend lives has only two rooms.
2. The room *who* / *that* is my favourite is my bedroom.
3. The family *where* / *who* live next door to me are really nice.
4. The street *where* / *that* I live is very quiet.
5. This is the armchair *which* / *who* my dad always sits on.
6. I have a friend *which* / *that* lives in the next street to me.

2 ●● Match the sentence halves.
1. [d] I really like the people
2. [ ] The kitchen is the only room in our house
3. [ ] The street
4. [ ] I have a friend
5. [ ] There are a lot of things
6. [ ] This is the sofa

a that I don't like.
b which I like about our home.
c where we all sit and watch TV in the evening.
d who live in our building.
e where we live is very beautiful.
f who lives in another city.

3 ●● Complete the sentences with one word in each gap.
1. I don't like the place *where* I live.
2. The thing _____ I like most about my bedroom is the bed.
3. My gran lives in a flat _____ has one bedroom.
4. I have a neighbour _____ plays loud music all the time.
5. This is the cupboard _____ we keep all the chocolate!
6. That's the family _____ used to live in our house.

4 ●● Order the words in brackets to complete the sentences.
1. That's the family *who live next door* (live/door/who/next).
2. The flat _____ (I/live/where) has three bedrooms.
3. The room _____ (most/like/that/I) is the living room.
4. The housework _____ (I/most/hate/which) is tidying my room.
5. The man _____ (lives/below/us/who) is very noisy.
6. I love _____ (place/live/where/I/the).

5 ●●● Complete the text with the missing words.

I love the place ¹*where* I live, and I love the people ²_____ I live with – my family. The flat ³_____ we live in isn't very big. There are three bedrooms. The big bedroom is ⁴_____ my parents sleep, and the small bedroom is ⁵_____ my sister sleeps. I love the view ⁶_____ we have from our bedroom window. We can see the sea! The only thing I don't like is the man ⁷_____ lives next door. I think he's someone ⁸_____ doesn't like children, because he's not very friendly to us.

Unit 5 — I can use defining relative clauses to describe people, things and places.

On the Portal
Extra Practice Activities: Lesson 5.2

5.3 Reading and Vocabulary
Storytelling

1 Read the story and answer the questions.
1. Who is the writer friends with?
   _____
2. What did they do last summer?
   _____
3. What was the surprise?
   _____

2 Complete gaps 1–4 with sentences a–d.
a. We played games together and had a great time.
b. On the day of the party, we all got up early.
c. I really can't sing well!
d. We all talked together quietly, waiting for the party to start.

3 Complete the sentences with the adverbs below.

badly   carefully   early   late
perfectly   ~~quietly~~   slowly   well

1. The children played *quietly* in their rooms.
2. Carry that bowl of soup _____ – it's hot!
3. I never get up _____ at the weekend because I like to sleep in.
4. My mum cooks lasagne _____. It's the best!
5. I'm tired because I went to bed _____ last night.
6. She sings very _____ and I don't like listening to her.
7. My brother eats really _____. It takes him ages to finish.
8. I can't draw pictures _____.

4 Choose the correct option.
1. Gina arrived (*late*)/ *lately* to school this morning.
2. You said it *wrong* / *wrongly*. It's not 'bit', it's 'beat'.
3. I worked really *hard* / *hardly* for this assignment.
4. Every weekend I wake up really *slow* / *slowly*.
5. The test was difficult, but I answered all the questions *right* / *rightly*.
6. My brother cooks *bad* / *badly*.

A STREET PARTY

I love the street where I live. I live at number 12, and I'm friends with the girls who live at numbers 5 and 9, so we always spend time together. But all the neighbours who live in my street are really friendly, and we often do things together.

Last summer we had a big street party. ¹____ I got ready in the morning nervously, because I really wanted it to be a success. We carefully prepared all the food for the party, and set it out on tables in the street. Jeff, the man who lives next door to us, has a big, long barbecue and he used it to cook burgers perfectly! During the morning, everyone came out slowly into the street. ²____ We also had lunch together and then we cleared the food away tidily. ³____ Then, in the afternoon, we had a surprise. The woman who lives at number 20 is a singer in a band, and the whole band came and played music for us in the street! Everyone sang along happily but not me. ⁴____

The party finished quite late in the afternoon, and then we all went back home. I was really tired, but it was a brilliant day. I hope we do it again this year.

I can understand a story about a personal experience.

5.4 Grammar

Modal verbs: *can, have to* and *must*

> **GRAMMAR** — Modal verbs: *can, have to* and *must*
>
> **Can** I borrow one of your dresses? (Is it OK?)
> You **can** read a poem. (It's OK.)
> You **can't** refuse. (It isn't OK.)
>
> **Do** I **have to** sing a song? (Is it necessary?)
> You **have to** try. (It's necessary.)
> You **don't have to** sing a song. (It isn't necessary.)
>
> You **mustn't** say 'yeah'. (Don't!)

1 ● Complete the sentences with *can* or *can't*.
1. I *can't* come round to see you tonight because my mum wants me to tidy my room.
2. We _____ use smartphones to go online.
3. You _____ borrow my tablet if you want.
4. _____ we look in the dictionary during the test?
5. I _____ learn to drive now because I'm too young.
6. My brother _____ watch TV until 11 p.m., but I _____. That's not fair!

2 ● Order the words in brackets to complete the sentences.
1. Do you *have to leave* (leave/have/to) soon?
2. My mum _____ (has/get/to/up) early.
3. I _____ (to/don't/tidy/have) my room.
4. Does your dad _____ (cook/have/to) every day?
5. My dog _____ (doesn't/sleep/have/to) outside.
6. Do you _____ (have/help/to) with the housework?

3 ●● Choose the correct answer.
1. We ____ give in this work before Thursday. We've got three days!
   a mustn't   **(b) don't have to**   c can't
2. You ____ shout at your brother. He didn't do anything.
   a mustn't   b don't have to   c can't
3. I ____ go on that website because I haven't got a password.
   a mustn't   b don't have to   c can't
4. You ____ join the photography club because it's full.
   a mustn't   b don't have to   c can't
5. Olly ____ work at the supermarket next weekend. It's a holiday.
   a mustn't   b doesn't have to   c can't
6. You ____ touch that key. It deletes everything!
   a mustn't   b don't have to   c can

4 ●●● Complete the dialogue with one word in each gap.
A: Hi! Do you have ¹*to* work this weekend?
B: No, I ²_____. I haven't got any work, so I ³_____ do what I want! Why?
A: It's my birthday and I ⁴_____ invite two friends to stay! Would you like to come?
B: Cool! Yes, please.
A: Can your sister Elise come too?
B: No, I'm afraid she ⁵_____. She was late home last week and now she ⁶_____ to stay home and help with the housework!
A: That's a shame. How long ⁷_____ she have to do that for?
B: Only for a week. Anyway – I ⁸_____ to go now. I ⁹_____ get to my next lesson.

Unit 5   52   I can use *can*, *have to* and *must* to talk about rules.

On the Portal
Extra Practice Activities: Lesson 5.4

5.5 Listening and Vocabulary
Describing your town

1 Look at photos 1–6 and complete the crossword.

[Crossword with 1 across: p a r k]

2 Write the words for the definitions.
1 You borrow books here. l i b r a r y
2 This is a place where a lot of people live in similar houses. e_ _ _ _ _ _ _ _
3 Some people go here to pray. c_ _ _ _ _ _
4 This is where the local government works. t_ _ _ _ h_ _ _ _
5 You can look at old things here. m_ _ _ _ _ _
6 You go here to send letters. p_ _ _ o_ _ _ _ _ _
7 You go here to watch a film. c_ _ _ _ _
8 You get information here when you're on holiday. t_ _ _ _ _ _ information centre.
9 You can buy new clothes here. s_ _ _ _ _ _ _ _ _ _ c_ _ _ _ _
10 You go here to report a crime. p_ _ _ _ _ s_ _ _ _ _ _

3 🔊 5.1 Listen to a conversation between James and Alice. Complete the notes with a word or a short phrase in each gap.

Paxford Tourist Information

Popular place to visit: The ¹*Mann* Art Gallery
Started in: ² _____
Location: next to the ³ _____
Ticket prices: Adults: £10.50
　　　　　　　　Students: ⁴ _____
Opening times: 9.30 a.m. to ⁵ _____ p.m.

4 🔊 5.1 Listen again. Tick (✓) the things Alice says there are at the art gallery.
1 ☐ a café
2 ☐ nice gardens
3 ☐ some statues
4 ☐ some Percy Mann paintings
5 ☐ pictures of Paxford town
6 ☐ a poster exhibition
7 ☐ a picture of a castle
8 ☐ some paintings of the sea
9 ☐ a gift shop

I can understand a conversation about a town.

On the Portal
Extra Practice Activities: Lesson 5.5

5.6 Speaking
Asking for, giving and receiving advice

1 🔊 **5.2 Listen and repeat the phrases.**

SPEAKING	Asking for, giving and receiving advice
Asking for advice Where should I go? What should I do? What do you think I should buy? Can you give me some advice? **Accepting advice** That's a good/brilliant idea. That's not a bad idea.	**Giving advice** You (really) should/shouldn't go there. I think/don't think you should visit him. Why don't you visit the museum? **Rejecting advice** That's a terrible idea! I don't think that's a good idea.

2 Complete the sentences with the words below.

> ~~advice~~   bad   good   really   should
> terrible   think   why

1 Can you give me some _advice_ about the best smartphones to buy at the moment?
2 That's a _____ idea. I really think it will work.
3 _____ don't you talk to your teacher about your problems?
4 Where _____ I go to buy some new trainers?
5 You _____ should try to fix your computer yourself.
6 What do you _____ I should wear to the party?
7 That's a _____ idea! I can't lie to my friends!
8 That's not a _____ idea.

3 Choose the correct response.
1 Where should I go on holiday?
   a I don't think that's a good idea.
   b What do you think I should do?
   (c) Why don't you go to France?
2 We should take the bus because it's quicker.
   a Why don't you visit the museum?
   b That's a brilliant idea.
   c Can you give me some advice?
3 Can you give me some advice about my room?
   a I think you should get some new posters.
   b That's not a bad idea.
   c What do you think I should do?
4 Why don't you have a break?
   a I think you should relax.
   b That's not a bad idea.
   c You really shouldn't do this.

4 Order the sentences to make conversations.
1 ☐ a Why don't you try the new store in the shopping centre?
   ☐ b That's a good idea. Thanks.
   [1] c I need to get a new smartphone. Where should I go to get one?
2 ☐ a You should get her a new book. I often buy books for presents.
   ☐ b That's a terrible idea! She hates books!
   ☐ c It's my sister's birthday tomorrow. What do you think I should get her?

5 🔊 **5.3 Complete the dialogue with sentences a–g. Then listen and check.**

Luke: Hi! How's the new school?
Jenny: It's OK. I started last week. The lessons are fine, but I don't know anyone. ¹ _d_
Luke: It's always hard when you start a new school. ² ____ You can meet people who have the same hobbies as you.
Jenny: ³ ____ There's an art club I can try.
Luke: ⁴ ____ Everyone likes people who have parties!
Jenny: ⁵ ____ Our house is very small. And Dad is still painting it.
Luke: Maybe your new friends can help!
Jenny: But I don't have new friends!
Luke: ⁶ ____ You can ask them about where to go in town. People like giving advice.
Jenny: ⁷ ____ Thanks! I feel better now.
Luke: No problem.

a That's a brilliant idea!
b That's not a bad idea.
c Why don't you ask some classmates to go shopping with you?
d ~~What do you think I should do to make friends?~~
e And why don't you have a party?
f I think you should join an after-school club.
g I don't think that's a good idea.

5.7 Writing
An informal email

1 Complete the email with the words below.

care   far   flat   guess   on   have
in (x2)   seems   well   ~~you~~

To: claire@email.com

Hi Claire,

How are ¹*you*? I hope you're ² _____ and that you passed all your exams! I'm fine. ³ _____ what! I'm in France! I'm staying with my French friend Jacques for a week and it's amazing.

He lives in a small village. It's called Beauchamp. It's ⁴ _____ the north of France and it's not ⁵ _____ from the sea. There aren't many houses or shops, but there's a café and a small supermarket. It ⁶ _____ nice. There isn't a train station, but you can catch a bus to the next town.

Jacques lives with his family in a lovely ⁷ _____. It's ⁸ _____ the third floor. It's in a very old house, but everything inside is modern. I really like the high ceilings and big windows. It's ⁹ _____ a very quiet street. From his bedroom window you can see across the countryside. It's really beautiful.

I ¹⁰ _____ to go now because Jacques' mum is calling me for dinner. The food here is wonderful!

Take ¹¹ _____!
Ryan

---

2 Read the email and answer the questions.

1 How long is Ryan staying in France?
   _____

2 What does he say there is in the village?
   _____

3 What does he like about the flat?
   _____

3 Read the email again. Match paragraphs 1–4 with the information in points a–e. One paragraph gives two pieces of information.

a ☐ a description of Jacques' home
b ☐ some news in Ryan's life
c ☐ a reason for finishing the email
d ☐ a question about Claire's life
e ☐ a description of Jacques' town

4 Write the opposites of the adjectives.

1 small   *big*
2 modern   _____
3 comfortable   _____
4 dark   _____
5 beautiful   _____
6 tidy   _____

WRITING TIME

5 Imagine you stayed with a friend in another town or village. Write an email to tell your friend about the town.

1 Find ideas
Make notes about:
- the town or village where you're staying.
- some interesting places and what they look like.
- your flat/house and the things that you like about it.

2 Plan and write
- Organise your ideas into paragraphs. Use Ryan's email to help you.
- Write a draft email.

3 Check
- Check language: did you use adjectives to describe places?
- Check grammar: did you use the correct relative pronouns?
- Write the final version of your email.

I can write an informal email.

My Language File

WORDLIST 🔊 5.4

Things in the home
armchair (n) _____
bathroom (n) _____
bedroom (n) _____
bedside table (n) _____
bookcase (n) _____
ceiling (n) _____
coffee table (n) _____
cooker (n) _____
cupboard (n) _____
curtains (n) _____
dishwasher (n) _____
floor (n) _____
fridge (n) _____
hall (n) _____
iron (n) _____
kitchen (n) _____
light (n) _____
living room (n) _____
microwave (n) _____
mirror (n) _____
plant (n) _____
roof (n) _____
rug (n) _____
shower (n) _____
sink (n) _____
sofa (n) _____
vacuum cleaner (n) _____
wardrobe (n) _____
washing machine (n) _____

Prepositions of place
above (prep) _____
behind (prep) _____
between (prep) _____
in (prep) _____
in front of (prep) _____
near (prep) _____
next to (prep) _____
on (prep) _____
opposite (prep) _____
under (prep) _____

Word friends (housework)
clean the floor _____
do the cooking _____
do the ironing _____
do the shopping _____
do the washing _____
do the washing up _____
dry the dishes _____
make your bed _____
put on the dishwasher _____
sort the rubbish _____
take out the rubbish _____
tidy your room _____
vacuum the floor _____

Adverbs of manner
badly (adv) _____
carefully (adv) _____
early (adv) _____
fast (adv) _____
hard (adv) _____
late (adv) _____
nervously (adv) _____
noisily (adv) _____
perfectly (adv) _____
quickly (adv) _____
quietly (adv) _____
right (adv) _____
slowly (adv) _____
well (adv) _____
wrong (adv) _____

Places in town
art gallery (n) _____
café (n) _____
castle (n) _____
church (n) _____
cinema (n) _____
estate (n) _____
hotel (n) _____
library (n) _____
museum (n) _____
park (n) _____
police station (n) _____
post office (n) _____
shopping centre (n) _____
station (n) _____
tourist information centre (n) _____
town hall (n) _____

Extra words
beautiful (adj) _____
big (adj) _____
bright (adj) _____
building (n) _____
comfortable (adj) _____
depressing (adj) _____
dining room (n) _____
downstairs (adv) _____
excitedly (adv) _____
flat (n) _____
garden (n) _____
happily (adv) _____
house (n) _____
live next door _____
modern (adj) _____
neighbour (n) _____
old-fashioned (adj) _____
place (n) _____
redecorate (v) _____
room (n) _____
rule (n) _____
shelf (n) _____
small (adj) _____
summer camp (n) _____
tent (n) _____
tidily (adv) _____
tidy (adj) _____
ugly (adj) _____
uncomfortable (adj) _____
untidy (adj) _____
view (n) _____
window (n) _____

Sounds good!
I'm fed up. _____
No wonder. _____
Keep it simple. _____

MY LANGUAGE NOTES

My favourite words/expressions from this unit

Unit 5 56

Self-check

Vocabulary

1 Choose the correct answer.
1. We keep all our plates in a big ____ in the kitchen.
   a cupboard   b bedside table   c wardrobe
2. My dad has a big ____ with more than 100 books!
   a bookcase   b coffee table   c armchair
3. The cat usually sleeps ____ the table.
   a over   b between   c under
4. I need a ____ for my bedroom floor.
   a rug   b cupboard   c sink
5. We have a big mirror ____ our sofa.
   a in   b under   c above
6. The ____ isn't working, so we can't cook.
   a fridge   b vacuum cleaner   c cooker
7. Turn the ____ on, it's dark in here.
   a light   b microwave   c shower

2 Choose the correct option.
1. I didn't *take / make* my bed this morning.
2. On Saturdays I *vacuum / tidy* the floor to help my parents.
3. We usually *do / make* the shopping on Friday evenings.
4. Can you *take out / put on* the dishwasher, please?
5. My sister never *washes / tidies* her room.
6. Dad *made / took* the rubbish out after dinner.
7. I *make / do* the washing and the ironing at home.

3 Complete the sentences with the correct words.
1. Our class went to the art g_____ last week.
2. My friend works at the police s_____.
3. The new shopping c_____ in town is brilliant.
4. There's a big meeting at the town h_____ about the new estate.
5. I must go to the post o_____ to send these letters.
6. Why don't we get some brochures from the tourist i_____ c_____?

Grammar

4 Choose the correct option.
1. The place *where / that* I go to school is nice.
2. The woman *where / who* lives next door is friendly.
3. The room *who / which* I like most is the kitchen.
4. We've got an old vacuum cleaner *that / who* never works!
5. That's the girl *who / where* I go to school with.
6. This is the building *which / where* I live.
7. That's the place *which / where* I like the most.
8. Maths is the subject *where / that* I like most.

5 Complete the sentences with the correct form of *can*, *must* or *have to*.
1. We _____ sit anywhere we like in class.
2. We _____ leave early because it's hot.
3. You _____ touch that dog. It's dangerous.
4. I _____ open the laptop. I forgot my password.
5. My dad _____ work on Saturdays, so we do the shopping on Sundays.
6. I _____ be late again! The teacher was angry with me yesterday.
7. You _____ eat more healthy food or you can get sick.

Speaking

6 Order the words in brackets to complete the dialogue.
A: Can you ¹_____ (some/advice/give/me)? I'm going to London with my friend.
²_____ (think/where/you/do) we should go?
B: I think you should go to a museum.
A: I don't think ³_____ (that's/idea/a/good). We don't like them.
B: OK! ⁴_____ (don't/you/go/why) to an art gallery?
A: ⁵_____ (for/thanks/advice/the).

YOUR SCORE
Vocabulary: __/20   Speaking: __/5
Grammar: __/15   Total: __/40

Look after yourself

VOCABULARY
Parts of the body | Sports and fitness | Accidents and injuries | Sleep | Symptoms, illnesses and allergies

GRAMMAR
Countable and uncountable nouns | Quantifiers | Past Continuous and Past Simple

6.1 Vocabulary
The body

1 ● Complete the labels for the parts of the body.

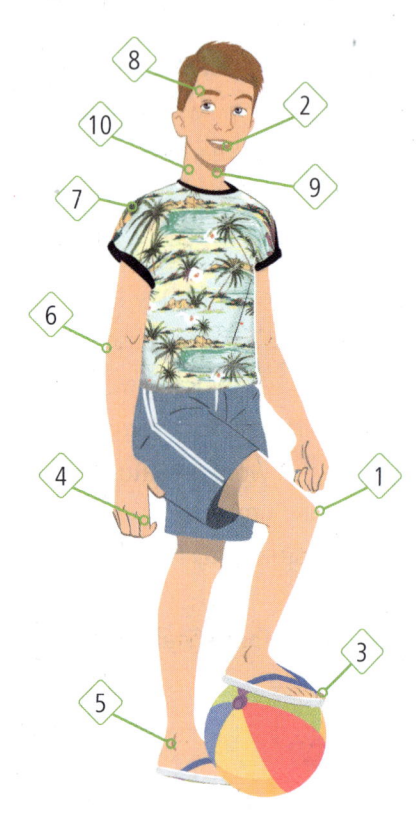

1 _k n e_ e
2 __i__s
3 ___ e s
4 __i___ e s
5 __k___
6 _____ w
7 ___ u___ r
8 _____ w
9 _____ t
10 ___ k

2 ● Complete the sentences with the words below.

elbow   fingers   knee   shoulders   throat   ~~toes~~

1 These shoes are too small. They hurt my _toes_.
2 Children like to paint with their _____ – they don't like using brushes.
3 My little sister likes sitting high up on my dad's _____.
4 My gran drinks a lot of warm water. She says it's good for her _____.
5 I hurt my leg last week and I now can't bend my _____.
6 I hit the desk with my arm and hurt my _____ when I fell.

3 ●● Choose the correct option.
1 Use your (brain) / neck and think hard!
2 My eyebrow / skin went brown in the sun.
3 After the race my stomach / heart was beating very fast.
4 Jack goes to the gym to get bigger bones / muscles.
5 A skeleton is just the bones / muscles of a person.
6 I can't eat any more. My lips / stomach is full.
7 I drank some hot tea too quickly and now my skin / tongue is sore.

4 ●● Choose the correct answer.
1 An adult has 206 ____.
   a muscles   (b) bones   c skin
2 The ____ on your body covers an average of two square metres.
   a muscle   b stomach   c skin
3 Your ____ is only one part of your digestive system, located in the middle.
   a heart   b brain   c stomach
4 A woman's ____ beats slightly faster than a man's.
   a heart   b brain   c stomach
5 The ____ around the heart work harder than all the other ones in the body.
   a skin   b muscles   c bones
6 Twenty percent of the blood and oxygen in our bodies goes to the ____.
   a brain   b tongue   c skin
7 The average human ____ is about 7.5 cm long.
   a tongue   b skin   c bones
8 The ____ is a part of the body that doesn't feel pain.
   a tongue   b brain   c neck

Unit 6   58

5 **WORD FRIENDS** Match sentences 1–4 with photos A–D.

A
B
C
D

1. [D] Mark does weight-training at the gym every day.
2. [ ] Emily plays football for the school team.
3. [ ] Ellie keeps fit at home.
4. [ ] Jake goes running every day.

6 Match the sentence halves.
1. [e] My brother hurt
2. [ ] I burnt my
3. [ ] Jake hit his
4. [ ] My friend fell off his bike and broke his
5. [ ] Amanda cut

a her finger with that knife by accident.
b arm while I was cooking.
c hand.
d head on the door.
e ~~his ankle while he was playing basketball.~~

I can talk about the body, sport and keeping fit.

7 Choose the correct answer.
1. Grant has got blond hair but dark ____.
   a elbows   (b) eyebrows   c ears
2. Jenny fell and hurt her ____ while she was playing football.
   a bones   b heart   c knee
3. People who can't hear sometimes watch people's ____.
   a lips   b nose   c teeth
4. I never ____ running before school.
   a keep   b go   c do
5. My uncle ____ weight-training twice a week at the gym.
   a plays   b does   c keeps
6. I haven't got very big ____ in my arms.
   a skin   b muscles   c fingers
7. I can carry my new leather bag over my ____.
   a neck   b knee   c shoulder
8. I ____ my mouth drinking that soup. It was very hot!
   a broke   b cut   c burnt

8 Complete the text with the words below.

bone   does   foot   has   hurt   muscles   ~~play~~   skin   toes

Tennis players often get problems when they ¹*play* tennis regularly. One of my friends ² _____ lessons every week. She also ³ _____ lots of exercise and enters competitions nearly every weekend. She gets lots of injuries. She needs new shoes because she has a bad ⁴ _____ – that's because she jumps up and down a lot. She also ⁵ _____ her head last month because another player hit her with a ball! When she plays in the summer her ⁶ _____ often goes very red. Last year she even broke a ⁷ _____ in her ankle because she fell over! And once someone hit the ball right on her foot and she broke two ⁸ _____. She usually needs a warm bath after playing because all her ⁹ _____ hurt. You think tennis is a safe game, but it may be sometimes quite dangerous!

On the Portal
Extra Practice Activities: Lesson 6.1

6.2 Grammar

Countable and uncountable nouns | Quantifiers

GRAMMAR Quantifiers

Countable	Uncountable
how many crisps?	how much chocolate?
too many tomatoes	too much salt
a lot of tomatoes	a lot of chocolate
some crisps	some chicken
not many crisps	not much sugar
not any chips	not any cream
not enough potatoes	not enough salt

1 ● Complete the table with the words below.

> banana bread cream crisps
> fruit hot dog meat potato
> salad salt sandwich sugar
> tomato vegetable water yoghurt

Countable nouns	Uncountable nouns
banana	bread

2 ●● Order the words in brackets to complete the sentences.
1. *How many apples* (many/apples/how) do you eat in a month?
2. I eat _____ (much/too/cake) at weekends.
3. There _____ (food/much/isn't) in the fridge.
4. _____ (salt/much/how) do you put on your food?
5. I've _____ (some/got/crisps) for lunch.
6. You should eat _____ (fruit/lot/a/of).
7. They _____ (chips/haven't/any/got) on the menu.
8. Do they _____ (nuts/any/sell) here?
9. There _____ (oranges/enough/aren't) for six people.
10. My mum makes _____ (many/sandwiches/too) for lunch.

3 ●● Complete the sentences with *some, any, much, many* and *a lot*.
1. A: How *many* sandwiches have you got today?
   B: I haven't got _____! We didn't have _____ bread at home, so I brought _____ crisps and fruit instead.
2. A: How _____ time did you spend on your homework?
   B: I didn't spend _____ of time on it. It was quite easy.
3. I didn't get _____ answers right in that exercise. Only two!
4. I ate too _____ food at breakfast. I feel ill!
5. You've got _____ of snacks today!

4 ●●● Complete the text with one word in each gap.

Healthy living?

[1] *Some* doctors think we eat [2] _____ many unhealthy snacks. For example we eat a [3] _____ of burgers and hot dogs because they're quick to eat and they don't cost [4] _____ money, and not [5] _____ healthy food. Schools are trying to encourage healthy eating habits. In some schools there aren't [6] _____ machines that sell snacks – not one! The students can't bring [7] _____ chocolate or crisps into school! They sell a [8] _____ of healthy food in the cafeteria. There is always [9] _____ salad, and a lot of fruit and vegetables, but unfortunately [10] _____ enough students eat them! [11] _____ students at these schools – not all – go out at lunchtime and don't buy [12] _____ healthy food. Instead they buy food like chips from local shops! So, what do you think we should do?

I can talk about quantities of food.

On the Portal
Extra Practice Activities: Lesson 6.2

6.3 Reading and Vocabulary
Sleep

1 Read the letter and put topics a–c in the correct order.
- a ☐ dreams
- b ☐ quality of sleep
- c ☐ how long we sleep

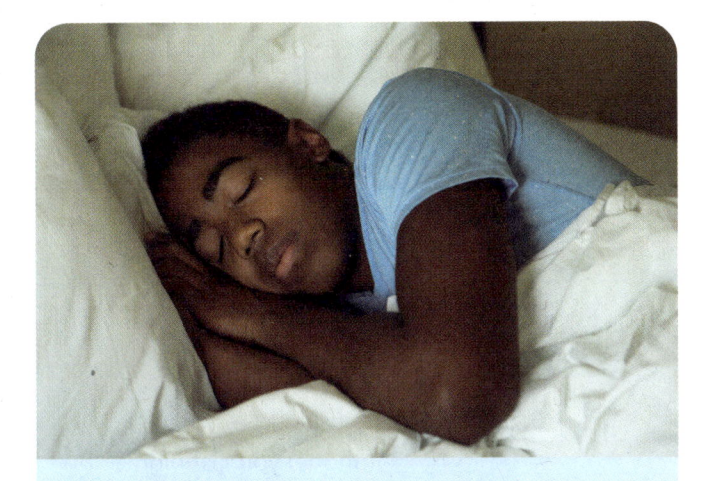

Dear Sleep Haters,

Stop hating it and start enjoying it! Here are some interesting facts to help you.

Humans sleep, on average, for around a third of their lifetime, but cats sleep for around two-thirds of theirs! How much sleep we get also depends on our age. Most adults need between seven and nine hours' sleep, but for teenagers that's not enough. They need between eight and ten hours. If you think that's a lot of sleep, then think about this: newborn babies typically sleep between fourteen and seventeen hours! This is because they are growing quickly.

We all dream after we fall asleep, but we don't always remember our dreams. In fact, just five minutes after waking up, we forget around fifty percent of our dreams. Interestingly, around twelve percent of people dream only in black and white.

How can we sleep better? Well, several studies show that doing exercise regularly helps us sleep better. But doing exercise just before bedtime can keep you awake. Another interesting fact is that you sleep better if you go to bed at the same time every night. If you don't, you can find it difficult to get to sleep. For some people this means that they feel sleepy all through the next day.

So, stop complaining and start sleeping.

Cheers,
The Experts.

I can understand an open letter about sleep.

2 Read the text again. Choose the correct answer.
1. Adults generally need
   - a more sleep than teenagers.
   - b less sleep than teenagers.
   - c nine hours' sleep.
2. Some people
   - a don't remember all of their dreams.
   - b never remember their dreams.
   - c remember all of their dreams.
3. Doing regular exercise can
   - a keep us awake.
   - b make us need more sleep.
   - c help us sleep well.
4. Other things that can keep some people awake are
   - a open windows.
   - b going to bed at different times on different days.
   - c feeling sleepy in the day.

3 **WORD FRIENDS** Complete the sentences with the words below.

| enough | fall | ~~feel~~ | go | keep | remember |
| up | well |

1. I sometimes *feel* tired when I get home from school, so I have a nap.
2. What time do you usually _____ to bed?
3. I always get _____ late at the weekend.
4. What things sometimes _____ you awake at night?
5. I never _____ my dreams. I'm sure they're interesting, though!
6. How long does it usually take you to _____ asleep?
7. I wish I could sleep more. I never feel like I get _____ sleep.
8. Good morning. Did you sleep _____ last night?

6.4 Grammar
Past Continuous and Past Simple

GRAMMAR — Past Continuous and Past Simple

+	I **was cycling** in the park. She **was jumping**. They **were playing** football.	
−	I **wasn't running**. She **wasn't swimming**. They **weren't playing** well.	
?	**Were** you **cycling**? **Was** she **jumping**? **Were** they **playing**?	Yes, I **was**./No, I **wasn't**. Yes, she **was**./No, she **wasn't**. Yes, they **were**./No, they **weren't**.
	What **was** she **doing** yesterday at 5 p.m.?	

Past Simple and Past Continuous
While/When/As I *was watching* the match, a dog *ran* in front of me.
I *was watching* the match when a dog *ran* in front of me.

1 ● Choose the correct option.
1 I (*wasn't*) / *didn't* talking to Danny when you saw me.
2 Jake *is* / *was* doing his homework during the lesson.
3 The students were *eating* / *eat* chips and salad.
4 *Was he* / *He was* playing well in the match?
5 *Was* / *Did* the teacher explaining a difficult grammar point?
6 You were having lunch when Sammy *arrived* / *was arriving*.

2 ●● Match the sentence halves.
1 [f] We were walking across the park
2 [ ] While I was eating my dinner
3 [ ] When I went downstairs
4 [ ] I fell asleep
5 [ ] Jack was singing a song in the concert
6 [ ] My brother wasn't skiing

a I dropped red sauce on my shirt.
b when he broke his ankle.
c Dad was cooking breakfast.
d when he fell off the stage.
e while I was reading my book.
f ~~when it started to rain.~~

3 ●● Complete the sentences with the Past Continuous or the Past Simple form of the verbs in brackets.
1 We *were eating* (eat) dinner outside when the rain *started* (start).
2 The students _____ (do) an exercise when the bell _____ (ring).
3 While I _____ (shop) on Saturday I _____ (meet) an old friend.
4 When I _____ (arrive) home my sister _____ (watch) a film on television.
5 I _____ (not look) when Paul _____ (fall) off his bicycle. I _____ (talk) to Marie.
6 What _____ (you/do) when I _____ (phone) you last night?

4 ●●● Complete the text with the correct past forms of the verbs below.

call	chat	fall	go (x2)	hurt	look
read	ride	say	see	not see	sit (x2)
start	~~wake~~				

A surprising meeting

When I ¹*woke* up yesterday my head ² _____, so I ³ _____ to see the doctor. I ⁴ _____ in the waiting room and I ⁵ _____ a magazine when suddenly someone ⁶ _____ 'Hello Pat!' I ⁷ _____ up and it was Terry Marsden. I last ⁸ _____ him five years ago at my first school! He ⁹ _____ down beside me and we ¹⁰ _____ chatting. Last week he ¹¹ _____ his horse when he ¹² _____ off! While we ¹³ _____, the doctor ¹⁴ _____ out 'Terry Marsden' and he ¹⁵ _____ in to see the doctor. I ¹⁶ _____ him later – I hope he was OK.

Unit 6 — 62
I can use the Past Continuous and the Past Simple to tell a story about past events.

On the Portal
Extra Practice Activities: Lesson 6.4

6.5 Listening and Vocabulary
Symptoms, illnesses and allergies

1 Complete the words in the sentences.
1. I'm feeling s _i_ _c_ _k_.
2. I've got a h__d_____.
3. I've got a s___e t_____t.
4. I've got a c_____.
5. I'm s__e____g.
6. I've got a s___m___h___e.
7. I've got hay f____r.
8. I've got a food a____r__y.
9. I've got a high t__p____t__e.
10. I've got the f___.
11. I have a c_____.

2 Complete the sentences with the correct words from Exercise 1.
1. In the summer I often sneeze because I get _hay fever_.
2. I worked on my computer for a long time and I had a _____.
3. If you get the _____, you should stay in bed.
4. I can't eat or drink anything because I've got a very _____.
5. I shouldn't eat fish because I've got a _____.
6. I ate too much and I felt _____.
7. Your face is hot and red. I think you've got a high _____.
8. Ah-ah-ah … Achoo! I'm s_____ because I have allergy to these plants.
9. I ate too many sweets and I had a _____.
10. My nose is running and I'm sneezing. I think I have a _____.
11. There's too much air pollution here. It feels like I've always got a _____.

3 🔊 6.1 Listen to Beth talking to Lloyd about a TV programme. Choose the correct answer.
1. The singing competition was on TV on
   a Friday.
   b Saturday.
   c Monday.
2. What was wrong with Viva in the show?
   a She had a sore throat.
   b She had a temperature.
   c She had a stomachache.
3. Mark
   a is always lucky in competitions.
   b gets nervous.
   c looked sick during the show.
4. The winner was
   a Johnny.
   b Mark.
   c Viva.
5. The winner receives
   a music lessons.
   b a lot of money.
   c a holiday.

4 🔊 6.1 Listen again and complete the sentences with one word in each gap.
1. Lloyd had football training on _____.
2. Johnny sang very _____.
3. Mark hurt his _____ in another competition.
4. The three singers are in a _____ after the competition.

I can understand a conversation about health problems.

6.6 Speaking
Talking about health problems

1 🔊 6.2 Listen and repeat the phrases.

> **SPEAKING** **Talking about health problems**
>
> **Asking what the problem is**
> What's the matter?
> What's wrong?
> How are you feeling?
>
> **Talking about symptoms**
> I feel sick/ill/terrible.
> I've got a stomachache/a headache/toothache/a temperature/
> a sore throat/a cold/the flu.
> My leg/back hurts.
> It's sore/painful.
>
> **Giving advice**
> Sit down.
> Have some water.
> You should/need to lie down/stay in bed/keep calm/see a doctor/
> be more careful/go to hospital.
> You should take a tablet/some medicine.

2 Choose the correct option.
1. John, you're yellow! What's the *wrong /* (*matter*)?
2. *What / How* are you feeling today, Mum?
3. I've got a fever and a cough. I think I've got the *cold / flu*.
4. I ate too much chocolate and now I feel *a headache / sick*.
5. She picked up a heavy box and now her *temperature / back* hurts.
6. Sit *on / down* and take a break. You look tired. *Have / Take* some water too.
7. You should stay *at the doctor / in bed* until you feel better.
8. You should take some *tablet / medicine* for your sore throat.
9. I think I'm going to faint – I need to lie *down / up*.
10. You should *go / take* to hospital if your leg hurts that much.

3 Order the words in brackets to complete the sentences.
1. *I feel* (feel/I) ill.
2. I've got _____ (bad/toothache/a).
3. _____ (take/should/you) a tablet.
4. You _____ (careful/more/should/be).
5. You _____ (in/bed/stay/should).
6. _____ (broken/got/a/I've) leg.

4 Complete the dialogues with the correct words below.

> a tablet   feel   feeling   hay fever
> lie   should   sneeze   terrible   what's
> ~~wrong~~

1. A: What's *wrong*?
   B: I _____ sick.
   A: You _____ go home.
2. A: How are you _____?
   B: I feel _____. My back hurts.
   A: You should _____ down.
3. A: _____ the matter?
   B: I've got a headache and I _____ a lot. I think I've got _____.
   A: You should have some water and then take _____.

5 🔊 6.3 Complete the dialogue with sentences a–f. Then listen and check.

A: ¹ *e*
B: I fell off my bicycle and my back hurts a bit.
A: ² ____
B: OK, thanks. I hit my head and that hurts too.
A: ³ ____
B: Thanks. Can I have some water with it?
A: ⁴ ____
B: Oh dear! That's making me feel sick now.
A: ⁵ ____
B: Oh, and now I can't feel my leg!
A: ⁶ ____

a. I've got some tablets for headaches. You should take one of these.
b. OK. Forget the doctor. You should go to hospital!
c. Come here and sit down for a moment.
d. That's bad. You should see a doctor.
e. ~~What's the matter? You look terrible.~~
f. Sure. Here you are.

Unit 6 | 64 | I can talk about health problems.

On the Portal
Extra Practice Activities: Lesson 6.6

6.7 Writing
A narrative

1 Read the story and answer the questions.
1 Where was Liz on holiday?
_____
2 What was the weather like?
_____
3 What went wrong on the journey?
_____
4 What happened in the end?
_____
5 Why was the journey disappointing?
_____

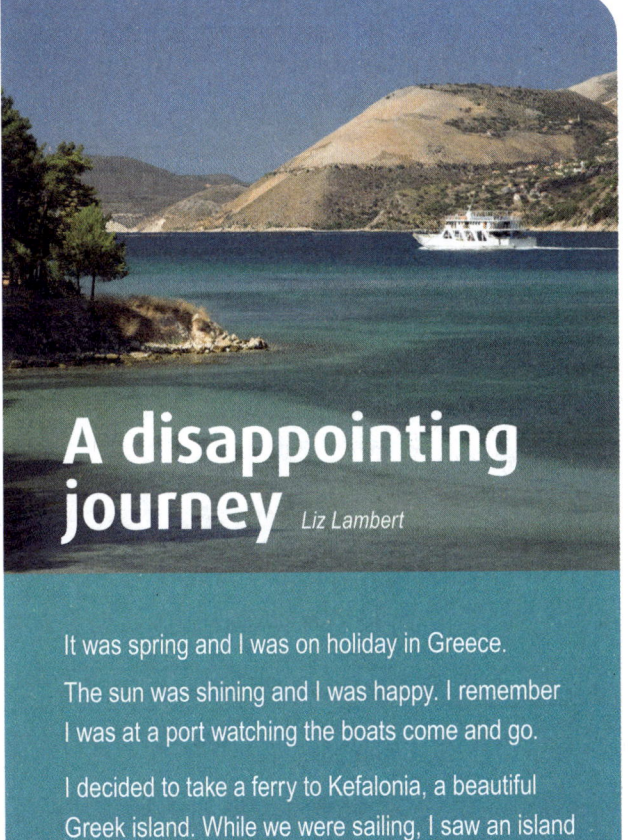

2 Match sentences a–d with narrative sections 1–4.
1 [d] Write when and where the event happened
2 [ ] Describe the scene
3 [ ] Describe the action
4 [ ] Write what happened in the end

a In the end, I never saw Kefalonia.
b The sun was shining and I was happy.
c Suddenly, I realised I was alone.
d ~~It was spring and I was on holiday in Greece.~~

3 Choose the correct option.

¹*When* / *Then* I was cycling home, I saw a big car stop outside my school. I stopped to have a look. ²*When* / *Then* a man got out of the car. I knew he was famous. ³*Next* / *A minute later* he was talking to the head teacher in the school yard. ⁴*Suddenly* / *While*, he turned around and said, 'Hi.' It was the singer Sam Smith! He was visiting his old school. I took a selfie with him. The ⁵*next day* / *after* I showed everyone the photo.

A disappointing journey
Liz Lambert

It was spring and I was on holiday in Greece.

The sun was shining and I was happy. I remember I was at a port watching the boats come and go.

I decided to take a ferry to Kefalonia, a beautiful Greek island. While we were sailing, I saw an island in the distance. Ten minutes later, we arrived there. Then I got off the boat with one other person. Next, I walked to some old buildings and some shops. Suddenly, I realised I was alone.

After an hour I met someone who explained that I was in Ithaki, not Kefalonia! He said there was a boat in thirty minutes, the last boat for the day. Twenty minutes later, I got on the boat back to the mainland. In the end, I never saw Kefalonia.

It was a truly disappointing journey!

WRITING TIME

4 Write a narrative with the title: *A really bad day.*

1 Find ideas
Make notes for a narrative.
• Where and when did the story happen?
• What was happening when the story began?
• What happened?
• How did it end?

2 Plan and write
• Organise your ideas into paragraphs. Use Liz's story to help you.
• Write a draft narrative.

3 Check
• Check language: did you use linkers to connect your sentences?
• Check grammar: did you use the Past Simple and the Past Continuous?
• Write the final version of your narrative.

I can write a narrative.

My Language File

WORDLIST 🔊 6.4

Parts of the body 1
- ankle (n) _____
- elbow (n) _____
- eyebrow (n) _____
- fingers (n) _____
- knee (n) _____
- lips (n) _____
- neck (n) _____
- shoulder (n) _____
- throat (n) _____
- toes (n) _____

Parts of the body 2
- bone (n) _____
- brain (n) _____
- heart (n) _____
- muscle (n) _____
- skin (n) _____
- stomach (n) _____
- tongue (n) _____

Word friends (sport and fitness)
- do exercises _____
- do sport _____
- do weight-training _____
- do yoga _____
- go cycling _____
- go running _____
- go surfing _____
- go swimming _____
- go walking _____
- keep fit _____
- keep healthy _____
- play badminton _____
- play basketball _____
- play football _____
- play hockey _____
- play rugby _____
- play (team) games _____

Word friends (accidents and injuries)
- break your leg _____
- burn your hand _____
- cut your finger _____
- hit your head _____
- hurt your ankle _____

Word friends (sleep)
- fall asleep _____
- feel sleepy _____
- feel tired _____
- get enough sleep _____
- get up early _____
- get up late _____
- go to bed _____
- go to sleep _____
- keep you awake _____
- remember your dreams _____
- sleep badly _____
- sleep well _____
- wake up early _____
- wake up late _____

Symptoms, illnesses and allergies
- cough (v) _____
- feel ill _____
- feel sick _____
- have a cold _____
- have a cough _____
- have a food allergy _____
- have a headache _____
- have a high temperature _____
- have a sore throat _____
- have a stomachache _____
- have hay fever _____
- have the flu _____
- sneeze (v) _____

Extra words
- accident (n) _____
- adult (n) _____
- advice (n) _____
- bleed (v) _____
- break your arm _____
- break your nose _____
- careful (adj) _____
- concentrate (v) _____
- cry (v) _____
- cut your hand _____
- doctor (n) _____
- exercise (v) _____
- fall (v) _____
- finish the race _____
- half marathon (n) _____
- healthy (adj) _____
- hormone (n) _____
- hospital (n) _____
- human (adj) _____
- hurt your back _____
- keep calm _____
- lie down _____
- medicine (n) _____
- memory (n) _____
- my fingers are stuck _____
- my leg/back hurts _____
- painful (adj) _____
- pay attention _____
- see a doctor _____
- sit down (v) _____
- stay in bed _____
- suddenly (adv) _____
- take a tablet _____
- take some medicine _____
- teenager (n) _____
- toothache (n) _____

Sounds good!
- Sure. _____
- What's going on? _____
- Let me have a look. _____

MY LANGUAGE NOTES

My favourite words/expressions from this unit

Self-check

Vocabulary

1 Write the words for the definitions.
1. Your food goes here. s_ _ _ _ _ _ _
2. This sometimes goes red in the sun. s_ _ _
3. You use this to think. b_ _ _ _ _
4. Your foot joins your leg here. a_ _ _ _ _
5. When you exercise a lot these get very strong. m_ _ _ _ _ _
6. These are at the end of your feet. t_ _ _
7. This is in the middle of your arm. e_ _ _ _
8. This is in the middle of your leg. k_ _ _

2 Choose the correct answer.
1. I try to eat well and ___ fit.
   a have   b do   c keep
2. I usually ___ to bed at 10.30 to get eight hours of sleep.
   a go   b make   c sleep
3. If I don't sleep well, the next day I ___ sleepy.
   a get   b feel   c go
4. I was really nervous and my ___ was beating very fast.
   a tongue   b brain   c heart
5. Doctors say it's important to ___ regular exercise.
   a make   b do   c play
6. I ___ my hand when I picked up that very hot plate.
   a cut   b burnt   c hit

3 Complete the sentences with the correct words below.

> allergy   flu   hay   headache
> temperature   throat

1. He needs to see the doctor because his _____ is very high.
2. I can't eat that. I've got an _____ to nuts.
3. In the summer I get terrible _____ fever.
4. The music at the concert was very loud and I got a _____.
5. We shouted a lot at the football match and now I've got a sore _____.
6. Olly has to stay in bed because he's got the _____.

Grammar

4 Complete the sentences with the correct words.
1. How _____ water do you drink every day?
2. There aren't _____ people here. Only two.
3. I didn't do _____ work last night! Nothing!
4. A _____ of people don't do any exercise and get ill.
5. Did you eat the cake? There _____ any left.
6. I answered _____ of the questions but not many.
7. How _____ apples have we got left?
8. We don't have _____ butter for this recipe, let's buy some more.

5 Choose the correct option.
1. Where were you and Sara going when I *saw / was seeing* you this morning?
2. Tim *read / was reading* a book when I called.
3. I wasn't working when he *came / was coming* to visit.
4. *Did you wait / Were you waiting* at the bus stop when it started to rain?
5. The teacher got angry because we *weren't / didn't* concentrating in class today.
6. *Were you / You were* eating when I called you?
7. I was leaving home when I *remembered / was remembering* to take my bag.

Speaking

6 Complete the dialogues with one word in each gap.
1. A: What's the _____?
   B: I _____ terrible.
   A: You _____ stay in bed.
2. A: How are you _____?
   B: My back _____.
   A: You should see a doctor.

YOUR SCORE

Vocabulary: __/20   Speaking: __/5
Grammar: __/15   Total: __/40

Reading Time 2

The Olympic Promise

There are two important things in young Nelson's life, running and his Granny Sarah. Is Nelson ready to run at the Olympic Games? And does he remember who he really is?

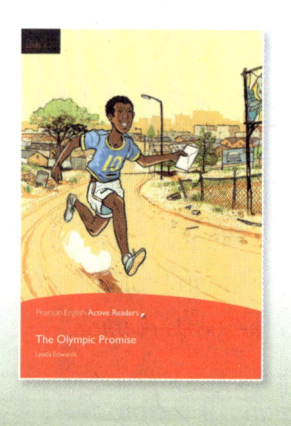

Nelson was in front again. He felt strong. One, two, one, two … and he was there! The winner! People shouted 'Nelson! Nelson!' He loved this feeling!

Nelson ran a lot of races before the Olympic Games and he won all of them. Now he was famous. People asked him questions on television and for the newspapers. They wanted to know about his life and his family. But Nelson didn't want to be the poor boy from a poor family. That wasn't his life now.

A television man came to Nelson after a race. 'Very good, Nelson! Are you going to win the marathon at the Olympics?'

Nelson smiled. 'I'm going to try!'

'You are from a poor family, Nelson. Was that difficult for you?' the man asked.

Nelson was angry. 'You're wrong,' he shouted. 'My father was a doctor and my mother was a teacher. We weren't poor. I had a good life!'

Ken listened to Nelson and the television man. He smiled. He was happy. Nelson's old life was in the past. The new Nelson was going to be famous in every country and his life was now with Ken.

Granny Sarah watched Nelson on television. She was very unhappy.

Nelson's friends and the people from his town were angry. 'Why did he say that?' they asked. 'He doesn't want to know us now because he's famous. We aren't important. Our lives are small.'

But Nelson was Sarah's boy. 'Listen!' she said. 'He's young. He's in a different town with different people. I know my boy – I know his heart. He's going to come back to us.'

But in her room at night Sarah cried.

Unit 6 68

Before you read

1 Match sentences a–d with their meanings 1–4.
- a ☐ It wasn't his life now.
- b ☐ He has good life.
- c ☐ Our lives are small.
- d ☐ I know his heart.

1. I know what a good person he is.
2. He isn't poor and doesn't have problems.
3. Our lives mean nothing because we are poor or not important.
4. His life now is different from his life in the past.

2 Look at the book cover and read the blurb. What do you think happens in the story?

While you read

3 🔊 RT2.1 Read and listen to the story. Choose the correct option.
1. Nelson *loses / wins* a lot of races.
2. He *speaks / doesn't speak* about his grandmother.
3. He becomes *happy / famous*.
4. He tells the *truth / lies* on television.
5. The people from his town are *happy / angry* when they see him on television.

4 Read the story again. Choose the correct answer.
1. Who is one of the main characters in the story?
   - a the journalist
   - b Granny Sarah
   - c Nelson's friends
2. What lie does Nelson tell?
   - a He's going to try and win the marathon at the Olympics.
   - b He's going to go back to his town.
   - c His family wasn't poor.
3. Why are the people from Nelson's town angry?
   - a Because Nelson makes them feel bad.
   - b Because Nelson is famous.
   - c Because Nelson's grandmother cries.

5 Mark the sentences T (true) or F (false). Then read the story again and check your answers.
1. ☐ Nelson won all of his races.
2. ☐ Nelson doesn't like being from a poor family.
3. ☐ Nelson was famous after the Olympic games.
4. ☐ The people from Nelson's town know the truth about Nelson's past.
5. ☐ Granny Sarah is angry.

After you read

6 Match adjectives 1–8 with their opposites a–h.

1 ☐ strong	a rich
2 ☐ poor	b new
3 ☐ difficult	c easy
4 ☐ angry	d weak
5 ☐ wrong	e unimportant
6 ☐ happy	f calm
7 ☐ old	g right
8 ☐ important	h unhappy

7 Choose the correct option.
1. In the past Nelson was *poor / rich*, but he was *strong / old*.
2. Granny Sarah was *angry / unhappy* when she saw Nelson on TV.
3. The people in Nelson's town were *important / angry*.
4. Nelson is *famous / weak* now.

8 **WRAP UP** Complete the information about the story.

Title: _____
Type: *crime story / love story / sport story*
Main characters: _____
_____
Important sport: _____
My opinion: ☆☆☆☆☆

Spending and saving

7 7.1 Vocabulary
Shopping

VOCABULARY Types of shops | Containers | Shopping centres | Eco-friendly shopping | Money | Pocket money

GRAMMAR Comparatives and superlatives of adjectives | *Going to* and Present Continuous for the future

1 ● Look at the photos and complete the names of the shops where you can buy these things.

1 n<u>ewsagent</u>'s
2 b_____
3 s_____ s_____
4 b_____'
5 f_____'
6 b_____
7 g_____'
8 c_____ s_____
9 p_____
10 c_____

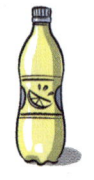

2 ●● Complete the sentences with the words below.

~~bakery~~   butcher's   café   clothes shop
florist's   greengrocer's   newsagent's   pharmacy

1 We need some bread. Can you go to the <u>bakery</u>?
2 I bought some new jeans at the _____.
3 They sell lovely apples at the _____.
4 I want a magazine and some chocolate from the _____.
5 Please get some chicken from the _____.
6 I've got a bad headache. Can you get me some tablets from the _____?
7 It's Mum's birthday tomorrow. Let's get her some flowers from the _____.
8 Let's have breakfast at that new _____ in town.

3 ● **WORD FRIENDS** Match containers 1–5 with words a–e to make phrases.

1 [c] a packet of   a lemonade
2 [ ] a bottle of   b chocolates
3 [ ] a pair of   c ~~tissues~~
4 [ ] a box of   d flowers
5 [ ] a bunch of   e socks

4 ● Label pictures A–E with phrases from Exercise 3.

Unit 7   70

5 ●● Complete the sentences with the words below.

car park   ~~department store~~   escalator   food court
lift   multi-screen cinema   public toilets
shop assistant   shoppers   trolley

1 We went to the _department store_ and bought some new clothes and a lamp.
2 In the shopping centre the _____ and lift weren't working, so we had to use the stairs.
3 We bought a lot of things in the supermarket, so we needed a big _____ to carry it all.
4 The _____ was nearly empty, so it was easy to find a space for the car.
5 There are thousands of _____ at the new shopping centre every day.
6 There's a new sandwich bar in the _____ where we can have lunch today.
7 The _____ at the new shopping centre are always very clean!
8 There are new films showing at the _____. Let's go!
9 I couldn't find what I wanted, so I asked the _____ to help me.
10 We took the _____ to the fifth floor because the escalators weren't working.

6 ●● Choose the correct answer.

1 The escalator is broken. Let's use the ___.
 a shopper   b car park   **c** lift
2 We had lunch in the ___ at the shopping centre.
 a escalator   b café   c book shop
3 My favourite shop in the shopping centre is the big ___ store.
 a food   b department   c public
4 We got these lovely flowers at the ___.
 a bakery   b florist's   c butcher's
5 I can't wash my hair with shampoo because the ___'s empty.
 a jar   b bar   c bottle
6 That ___ was very helpful and friendly.
 a trolley   b shop assistant   c lift
7 You shouldn't eat so many ___ of crisps!
 a jars   b packets   c boxes
8 We need to buy quite a lot of things, so can you get a ___, please?
 a trolley   b escalator   c shopper

7 ●●● Complete the text with the words below.

bakery   bottles   box   butcher's   court
~~greengrocer's~~   newsagent's   newspaper   shoppers

Hi Brian!

Thanks for doing the shopping today. We need lots of things for the party tomorrow. First can you go to the ¹_greengrocer's_ and get some oranges and a big ² _____ of tomatoes, please? Then go to the ³ _____. Your dad wants a ⁴ _____, and get a magazine for me, please! Can you also get some bread from the ⁵ _____ in the food ⁶ _____ in the shopping centre? I love their bread! If you get a chicken from the ⁷ _____, I can cook it and use it for sandwiches tomorrow. And three or four ⁸ _____ of lemonade. I think that's all! I don't think there are many ⁹ _____ at the centre today, so it shouldn't be too busy.

Mum x

I can talk about types of shops and shopping centres.

7.2 Grammar

Comparatives and superlatives of adjectives

GRAMMAR — Comparatives and superlatives of adjectives

quick	quicker	the quickest
nice	nicer	the nicest
big	bigger	the biggest
friendly	friendlier	the friendliest
important	more important	the most important
good	better	the best
bad	worse	the worst

They are bigger than my local shops.
They are not as cheap as the shopping centre.

1 ● Complete the sentences with the correct forms of the adjectives in brackets.
1. This film is *older* (old) than that one.
2. It's _____ (warm) today than it was yesterday.
3. Which river is _____ (long) in the world?
4. The phone signal is _____ (good) here than inside the house.
5. Shopping in a shopping centre is _____ (expensive) than shopping at a market.
6. I think buying things online is _____ (bad) than buying things in small local shops.

2 ●● Make three sentences for the pairs of adjectives 1–3.

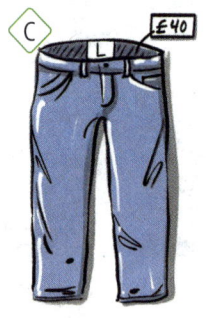

1. small/big
   A is *smaller than* B.
   B is *bigger than* A.
   C is *the biggest* pair of trousers.
2. short/long
   A is _____ B.
   B is _____ A.
   C is _____ pair of trousers.
3. cheap/expensive
   A is _____ B.
   B is _____ A.
   C is _____ pair of trousers.

3 ●● Complete the second sentence with *as … as* so that it means the same as the first one.
1. I'm taller than my brother.
   My brother isn't *as tall as* me.
2. It's colder in Scotland than it is here.
   Here it isn't _____ it is in Scotland.
3. This programme is more interesting than the programme last night.
   The programme last night wasn't _____ this programme.
4. Your jeans were more expensive than mine.
   My jeans weren't _____ yours.
5. This bed is more comfortable than my old one.
   My old bed wasn't _____ this one.
6. My sister's bedroom is tidier than mine.
   My bedroom isn't _____ my sister's.

4 ●●● Complete the email with the correct forms of the adjectives.

Hi Grace,

Thank goodness – our end of year tests are finished! I'm ¹*happier* (happy) than I was this time last year. Geography was ² _____ (easy) than before and French was ³ _____ (good) too. But IT was horrible. The paper definitely wasn't as ⁴ _____ (long) as last year's, but it was ⁵ _____ (difficult). Last year I was ⁶ _____ (bad) in the class! I don't want to be that bad again! My friend Tina is ⁷ _____ (good) student in my class, but I get ⁸ _____ (high) marks than her for English! Last night I was very stressed, but now I'm ⁹ _____ (relaxed). My friends and I want to find ¹⁰ _____ (busy) restaurant in town and have pizza together.

Katy

I can use the comparative and superlative of adjectives to describe things.

On the Portal
Extra Practice Activities: Lesson 7.2

7.3 Reading and Vocabulary
Planet-friendly shopping

1 Read the article and complete the sentences with a short phrase in each gap.
1. People who work at the art shop tell Maria about _____.
2. Dylan loves the charity shop in his area because the prices are _____.
3. Emel doesn't use plastic bags because she _____.

THE BEST PLACES TO SHOP

What's your favourite place to shop, and why?
We asked three people around the world to share their best places to shop and why.

1 Maria, Spain
My favourite shop is in a shopping centre near where I live. It's a planet-friendly shop which sells art and other little things which are all recycled. It's not as big as other shops in the centre, but the people who work there are nice to all their customers! I go there quite often and they know me, so they always show me the new things they have and tell me about their special offers.

2 Dylan, UK
I love the charity shop in my High Street. There are lots of charity shops in my area, but this one always has the best stuff, and the prices are always lower than in other shops. A month ago, I bought a really cool pair of trainers which are much more expensive when you buy them new.

3 Emel, Turkey
The place where I like to shop most in my city is the central market. It's the biggest market in the area. I love the sounds, colours and smells, and the food is always fresh. I care about the environment, so I don't use plastic bags. I have a cloth bag which I fill with delicious fruit and vegetables every time I go there, then I get the bus home. It's the best place in my city, I think!

I can understand an article about shopping habits.

2 Read the article again. Match paragraphs 1–3 with questions a–f. There are two questions which match each paragraph.
a ☐ Which person says that their favourite place to shop is cheap?
b ☐ Which person describes how they travel to/from their favourite place to shop?
c ☐ Which person doesn't live far from their favourite shop?
d ☐ Which person describes something they bought recently?
e ☐ Which person thinks the people who work in the shop are friendly?
f ☐ Which person describes the quality of the things they can buy?

3 Complete the sentences with the words below.

charity shop	customers	environment
planet-friendly	cloth bags	~~price~~
recycle	special offers	

1. Only £5? That's a really good *price* for those trainers!
2. I always look for _____ in the supermarket, like buy two and get one free.
3. I buy lots of second-hand books from my local _____.
4. A really _____ way to shop is to take your own bags.
5. The assistants in that shop are always very friendly to their _____.
6. Make sure you _____ that bottle when you finish with it.
7. I always use _____ when I go shopping. They're really good for the _____.

7.4 Grammar

Going to and Present Continuous for the future

GRAMMAR — *Going to* and Present Continuous for the future

- **Fixed arrangements**
  He*'s coming* home next week.
  She *isn't getting* the bus until three.
  Is she *coming* or not?

- **Intentions and future plans**
  She*'s going to look for* a new book.
  I'm not going to buy it.
  Are you *going to buy* a present?

1 ● Complete the sentences with the correct form of *going to* and the verbs in brackets.

1. I *'m going to phone* (phone) Laura later to ask about her exam.
2. We _____ (look) round the new shopping centre on Saturday morning.
3. _____ (your mother/get) a new car soon?
4. I _____ (not become) a doctor. I want to be a research scientist.
5. Dad _____ (get) a bigger computer for the family next month.
6. _____ (you/email) Sonia about the party?

2 ●● Complete the sentences with the correct Present Continuous form of the verbs below.

| have | open | ~~start~~ | play | not meet | fly |

1. My mum *'s starting* a new job on Monday.
2. It's my birthday on Saturday and I _____ a party at my house in the evening.
3. Which airport _____ you _____ from this weekend?
4. A famous actor _____ the new shopping mall on 16 June.
5. Sorry, my mistake! We _____ Jane at 6.00 but at 6.30.
6. Jake is really pleased. He _____ in the school football match on Friday.

3 ●● Complete the sentences with the *going to* or Present Continuous form of the verbs in bold.

1. My plan is to **ASK** Dad to lend me some money for a new laptop.
   I'm *going to ask Dad* to lend me some money for a new laptop.
2. The arrangement is for Leo and me to **CATCH** the same train tomorrow.
   Leo and I are _____ the same train tomorrow.
3. I want to **HAVE** a quick shower and then go out with Geoff.
   I'm _____ a quick shower and then go out with Geoff.
4. Jack's aim is to **WORK** hard for the next exams.
   Jack is _____ hard for the next exams.
5. The arrangement is for Dan and Kevin to **ARRIVE** at 7.00, not 8.00!
   Dan and Kevin aren't _____ at 8.00, but at 7.00.
6. Do you plan to **SPEND** a lot of money at the shopping centre on Saturday?
   Are you _____ a lot of money at the shopping centre on Saturday?

4 ●●● Complete the message with the *going to* or Present Continuous form of the verbs.

| bring | buy | do | go | ~~have~~ | play | show |

Nicky,

Let's arrange something for next week. My diary is quite full! I ¹ *'m having* a driving lesson on Monday at 4.30 and on Tuesday I ² _____ shopping with my gran at 4.00. She ³ _____ my birthday present and she wants me to choose it! I ⁴ _____ her round the new shopping centre in the High Street. Then on Wednesday I ⁵ _____ in a tennis match at lunchtime and in the evening Sally ⁶ _____ round some photos from her holiday to show me.
⁷ _____ you _____ anything on Thursday evening?

Speak soon x

Unit 7 — 74
I can use the Present Continuous and *going to* to talk about arrangements and plans for the future.

On the Portal
Extra Practice Activities: Lesson 7.4

7.5 Listening and Vocabulary
Saving and spending money

1 Write the words for the definitions.
1. a container with a lock where you can keep cash: m_o_ n _e_ y b_o_x
2. money that parents give children every week: p_ _ _ _ _ _ _ m_ _ _ _ _
3. a time when things are cheaper in the shops: s_ _ _ _
4. you keep your money in this when you go out: w_ _ _ _ _ _ / p_ _ _ _ _
5. the money that the assistant gives you back when you buy something: c_ _ _ _ _ _

2 **WORD FRIENDS** Match the sentence halves.
1. [e] When I was a child I
2. [ ] I went shopping yesterday and I
3. [ ] Some people think teenagers should
4. [ ] Kenny was very kind and he
5. [ ] Last year I was careful and I
6. [ ] Last month I lent Paul some money and yesterday he
7. [ ] My sister never has much money and often

a. spent a lot of money in the clothes shop in the town centre.
b. borrows some from me to go shopping.
c. lent me some money to buy a concert ticket.
d. saved enough money to buy a new car.
e. ~~got £8 pocket money every week.~~
f. paid me back.
g. earn their pocket money by helping their parents at home.

3 🔊 7.1 Listen to a conversation between Jenny and Harry. Complete the notes.

- Olly and Alexa are going to stay in a hotel in _London_.
- Jenny bought a new _____ last month.
- The current month is _____.
- Jenny has to buy the ticket _____.
- Harry suggests she gives some _____.

4 🔊 7.1 Listen again and choose the correct answer.
1. Which concert does Jenny want to go to?
   a. Ed Sheeran
   b. Dua Lipa
   c. Little Mix
2. When are Jenny's exams?
   a. in March
   b. in May
   c. in June
3. Who is going to buy the tickets?
   a. Alexa
   b. Olly
   c. Jenny
4. The tickets are going on sale at
   a. 1 o'clock.
   b. 2 o'clock.
   c. 3 o'clock.
5. How much does Jenny earn from babysitting now?
   a. £10
   b. £50
   c. £15
6. Where did Jenny live before?
   a. in London
   b. in the USA
   c. in Paris

I can understand a conversation about money.

7.6 Speaking
Shopping for clothes

1 🔊 **7.2** Listen and repeat the phrases.

SPEAKING	Shopping for clothes
Helping a customer	**Buying clothes**
Can I help you?	I'm looking for a blue shirt.
They're in the sale.	How much is this one/are these?
What size are you?	Can I try this/these on, please?
The changing rooms are over there.	It's/They're too big/small.
Here's your change.	Have you got it/them in a smaller/bigger size?
	Have you got it/them in another colour?
	I'll take it/this one.
	I'll take them/these ones.

2 Complete the sentences with the words below.

~~help~~   here   much   size   take   try

1 Can I _help_ you?
2 Can I _____ this on, please?
3 What _____ are you?
4 How _____ is it?
5 _____'s your change.
6 I'll _____ them.

3 Order the words in brackets to complete the sentences.

1 _I'm looking for_ (for/looking/I'm) a jacket.
2 Have you got them _____ (size/a/smaller/in)?
3 Can I _____ (on/this/try), please?
4 _____ (rooms/the/changing) are over there.
5 Have you got it _____ (colour/in/another)?
6 They're _____ (big/too).

4 Choose the correct option.

1 This coat is too big. Have you got a smaller (one)/ ones?
2 Do you want the cheap tickets or the expensive one / ones?
3 I love chicken sandwiches, but I don't like cheese one / ones.
4 This phone is very old. I'd like a newer one / ones.

5 Match questions 1–6 with answers a–f.

1 [a] Can I help you?
2 [ ] How much are these?
3 [ ] Can I try these on, please?
4 [ ] What size are you?
5 [ ] Have you got them in a smaller size?
6 [ ] Here's your change.

a ~~I'm looking for some jeans.~~
b Thank you.
c I'm sorry, we haven't.
d I'm size twelve.
e Sure, the changing rooms are over there.
f They're in the sale. They're fifteen pounds.

6 🔊 **7.3** Complete the dialogue with sentences a–h. Then listen and check.

SA: Hi there. Can I help you?
C: ¹ _g_
SA: These ones are in the sale.
C: ² ___
SA: They're twenty-five pounds. Do you like the brown ones?
C: ³ ___
SA: Yes. What size are you?
C: ⁴ ___
SA: Here you are. Size twelve.
C: ⁵ ___
SA: Sure. The changing rooms are over there.
C: ⁶ ___
SA: Try these. They're size fourteen.
C: ⁷ ___
SA: Great! They look really nice.
C: ⁸ ___
SA: Thanks. Don't forget your change.

a Mm … Have you got them in black?
b I'll take them.
c And they're twenty-five pounds? Here you are.
d They're nice. How much are they?
e Twelve.
f Thanks … Oh dear! They're too small.
g ~~Yes. I'm looking for some jeans.~~
h Great! Can I try them on?

On the Portal
Extra Practice Activities: Lesson 7.6

7.7 Writing
A message

1 Complete the sentences with the words below.

> can having ~~going~~ (x2) late let
> let's starting there would

Give information

I'm ¹*going* to the beach.
I'm ² _____ a party.
The bus is really ³ _____ .

Make a request, offer or invite

⁴ _____ you like to come?
⁵ _____ you help me finish this?

Make arrangements

⁶ _____ meet at the entrance to the park at 12.30.
The party is ⁷ _____ at 2 o'clock.
I'm ⁸ _____ to be at the tennis club at 7.30.

End the message

See you ⁹ _____ /soon.
¹⁰ _____ me know.

2 Use phrases from Exercise 1 and the information below to write short messages.

1 To Sara from Anna. Me and Danny – beach this afternoon. You / come? Leave / 2 o'clock.

Hi Sara,
Danny and I are going to the beach this
afternoon. Would you like to come?
We're leaving at about 2 o'clock.
Let me know.
Anna

2 To Anna from Sara. Yes, meet / outside house / 2.05. See / soon.

_____
_____
_____
_____

3 Complete the sentences with the correct phrases below.

> Perhaps we could   Please wait   Shall we
> ~~Would you like to~~

1 *Would you like to* come to the cinema tomorrow?
2 _____ meet after school?
3 _____ go to the theatre.
4 _____ at the bus stop for me.

4 Read the invitation (A) and the email (B). Then complete Lola's notes (C) with a word or a short phrase in each gap.

A

Come to Jake's
18th birthday barbecue
on Sunday at 1 Wood Lane
Starts at 12.30 and continues until ????
Please bring a plate of food – sausages/sandwiches?
Let me know if you can come by Thursday.
Jake

B

Hi Lola,

Hope you can come. Can you tell Alexa about it too, please? I haven't got her email address and she's off school at the moment. Dave and the others are meeting at the bus stop to get the 12.15 bus. Maybe you could meet up there?

Jake

C

Lola's Notes Barbecue
Person having barbecue: ¹*Jake*
Reason: ² _____   *Take:* ⁵ _____
Day: ³ _____   *Travel by:* ⁶ _____
Time: ⁴ _____   *Meet up at:* ⁷ _____

WRITING TIME

5 Use the information in Lola's notes to write a message to Alexa about the barbecue.

1 Find ideas
- Include the information in Lola's notes.

2 Plan and write
- Organise your ideas into paragraphs. Use the messages in Exercise 2 to help you.
- Write a draft message.

3 Check
- Check language: did you use polite phrases in your message?
- Check grammar: did you use the Present Continuous or *going to* for your arrangement?
- Write the final version of your message.

I can write a message to make an arrangement.

My Language File

WORDLIST 🔊 7.4

Shops
bakery (n) _____
bookshop (n) _____
butcher's (n) _____
café (n) _____
clothes shop (n) _____
florist's (n) _____
greengrocer's (n) _____
newsagent's (n) _____
pharmacy (n) _____
shoe shop (n) _____

Word friends (containers)
bottle of shampoo _____
box of chocolates _____
bunch of flowers _____
packet of tissues _____
pair of socks _____

Shopping centres
car park (n) _____
department store (n) _____
escalator (n) _____
food court (n) _____
lift (n) _____
multi-screen cinema (n) _____
public toilets (n) _____
shop assistant (n) _____
shopper (n) _____
trolley (n) _____

Eco-friendly shopping
charity shop (n) _____
cloth bag (n) _____
customer (n) _____

environment (n) _____
planet-friendly (adj) _____
price (n) _____
recycle (v) _____
special offer (n) _____

Money
change (n) _____
money box (n) _____
pocket money (n) _____
purse (n) _____
sales (n) _____
wallet (n) _____

Word friends (pocket money)
borrow money _____
earn your pocket money _____
get pocket money _____
lend money _____
pay (money) back _____
save money _____
spend money _____

Extra words
backpack (n) _____
be in the sale _____
busy (adj) _____
buy online _____
changing room (n) _____
cheap (adj) _____
climbing wall (n) _____
concert ticket (n) _____
Excuse me. _____
expensive (adj) _____
fresh (adj) _____

gift shop (n) _____
give presents _____
go into town _____
go out for a meal _____
good choice of _____
homemade (adj) _____
hurry up (v) _____
internet shopping (n) _____
keep money in your pocket _____
kind to the planet _____
local shop (n) _____
look for (v) _____
make a list _____
market (n) _____
out of town _____
pay for (v) _____
present (n) _____
quality (n) _____
reuse (v) _____
sail (v) _____
second-hand (adj) _____
sell online _____
sense of humour (n) _____
shop around (v) _____
shop online _____
shopping list (n) _____
size (n) _____
throw away (v) _____
water bottle (n) _____

Sounds good!
Hurry up. _____
I'm off. _____
Wait for me! _____

MY LANGUAGE NOTES

My favourite words/expressions from this unit

Self-check

Vocabulary

1 Complete the words in the sentences.
1. A: Where can you buy a b___ of cakes?
   B: At the b_____.
2. A: Where can you buy a p_____ of crisps?
   B: At the n_____'__.
3. A: Where can you buy a b_____ of shampoo?
   B: At the p_____.
4. A: Where can you buy a p____ of boots?
   B: At the s____ s____.

2 Complete the sentences with the words below.

| court | department | escalator | park |
| multi-screen | shopper | toilets | trolley |

1. The _____ wasn't working, so we used the stairs.
2. We had a lot of food to buy and our _____ was full.
3. We had a meal in the food _____.
4. I like _____ stores because they have a lot of different things.
5. Can you tell me where the public _____ are, please?
6. I was the last _____ in the supermarket before they closed.
7. We drove to the shopping centre, but couldn't find a space in the car _____.
8. Let's watch a film at the _____ cinema.

3 Complete the words in the sentences.
1. My young sister gets £5.00 _____ money a week from our parents.
2. I think you gave me the wrong _____. I gave you ten pounds.
3. Excuse me, what's the _____ of the jeans?
4. The supermarket has a special _____ on pizzas – buy one and get one free.
5. Do you put your money in a _____ box?
6. My dad left his _____ in the shop. There was a lot of money in it!
7. Do you use a cloth _____ to carry your shopping home?
8. We _____ all our paper and plastic.

Grammar

4 Complete the sentences with the correct form of the adjectives in brackets.
1. Your book is _____ (boring) than my novel.
2. The new department store is _____ (big) than the old one.
3. *Flash* was _____ (enjoyable) film I saw last year.
4. My bed isn't _____ (big) as my sister's.
5. Mum's laptop was _____ (cheap) one in the shop.
6. English is _____ (difficult) language that I know! It is so hard.
7. My brother isn't _____ (nice) as yours.
8. My teacher is _____ (kind) person I know.

5 Complete the sentences with the *going to* or Present Continuous form of the verbs in brackets.

I ¹_____ (see) the doctor on Friday evening. I'm not sure about next week. My friends and I ²_____ (visit) the new museum. ³_____ (you/come) to the party on Saturday? Sue ⁴_____ (ask) some friends to come. I ⁵_____ (buy) a new dress or a skirt for the party. This weekend Jake ⁶_____ (play) tennis with Ian. I ⁷_____ (not go) because I have a lesson.

Speaking

6 Complete the dialogue with one word in each gap.

A: ¹_____ I help you?
B: Yes, I'm looking for some boots.
A: These ²_____ are on sale.
B: Can I ³_____ them on?
A: Of course. Here you are.
B: Oh, they're too small. Have you got a size 40?
A: Yes, here you are.
B: Thanks. I'll ⁴_____ them. Here you are.
A: Great. And here's your ⁵_____.

YOUR SCORE

Vocabulary: __/20   Speaking: __/5
Grammar: __/15   Total: __/40

Learning for the future

VOCABULARY
Jobs | Work collocations | World of work | Tests | School and education | Schoolwork

GRAMMAR
Will for future predictions | First Conditional

8.1 Vocabulary
Jobs and work

1 ● Match jobs 1–8 with photos A–H.

A 3
B ☐
C ☐
D ☐
E ☐
F ☐
G ☐
H ☐

1 architect
2 artist
3 ~~hairdresser~~
4 scientist
5 firefighter
6 pilot
7 lawyer
8 nurse

2 ● Match jobs 1–8 with definitions a–h.

1 *b* police officer
2 ☐ tour guide
3 ☐ IT specialist
4 ☐ care worker
5 ☐ builder
6 ☐ gardener
7 ☐ driver
8 ☐ journalist

a Someone who works with computers.
b ~~Someone who catches criminals.~~
c Someone who takes people to places in a car.
d Someone who writes articles for newspapers or news websites.
e Someone who builds things like houses.
f Someone who shows people around tourist attractions.
g Someone who looks after old or disabled people.
h Someone who looks after plants and flowers.

3 ●● Which jobs are the people talking about?

1 People come to me when they arrive at the hotel. I'm a *receptionist*.
2 I repair cars. I'm a _____.
3 I help ill people. I'm a _____.
4 I work in parliament and try to win elections. I'm a _____.
5 I bring people their food in a restaurant. I'm a _____.
6 I manage a team of people. I'm a _____.
7 I cook meals for people in my restaurant. I'm a _____.
8 I repair machines. I'm a _____.
9 I help people with their money and taxes. I'm an _____.

4 ● ● Complete the sentences with the words below.

> accountant doctor firefighter pilot
> police officer ~~scientist~~ tour guide waiter

1. My uncle is a *scientist* and he does experiments in a laboratory.
2. I'd like to be an _____ for a big company. I'm very good with numbers.
3. I was feeling ill, so I went to the see the _____.
4. I've got a summer job as a _____ in a café in town. I serve customers coffee and sandwiches.
5. It takes a long time to become a _____ and fly planes.
6. Someone stole my dad's car and a _____ came to our house today to ask questions.
7. I'd like to be a _____ and show tourists around interesting places and historic buildings.
8. A _____ has a dangerous job, but they save a lot of lives.

5 ● ● **WORD FRIENDS** Choose the correct option.

1. My mum is an accountant and works in (an office) / outdoors.
2. Are you happy at *work / team*?
3. I'd like to work *of / for* a big company.
4. Firefighters need to work *on time / in a team*.
5. Receptionists usually work *indoors / outdoors*.
6. I'd love to work *as / at* a scientist.

6 ● ● Complete the sentences with the words below.

> alone earn for happy team time
> weekend ~~work~~

1. Firefighters don't have to *work* in an office.
2. Most managers work _____ a company.
3. Artists usually work _____.
4. I think it's important to be _____ at work.
5. Lawyers can _____ good money.
6. I need to get up early to get to work on _____.
7. My dad's a doctor and he often has to work at the _____.
8. In a hospital nurses have to work in a _____.

I can talk about people and their jobs.

7 ● ● ● Complete the text with one word in each gap.

Work in college
12/04/2021

I'm still a student, but I have a part time ¹*job*. I'm a ² _____ at a restaurant in my town. I take the meals from the kitchen to the customers. I like my job. I don't earn much ³ _____, but it's fun. It's nice to work ⁴ _____ a team and I like the ⁵ _____ a lot. He cooks great food! I have to work at the ⁶ _____, so I can't go out a lot with my friends on Saturdays and Sundays. I also have to wear a black and white uniform, but that's OK! In the future I'd like to be a ⁷ _____ like my dad and work for a newspaper, or an ⁸ _____ like my mum and design houses. I think it's important to work when you're a student. You learn lots of things, like – it's important to ⁹ _____ to work on time. Also, it's important to be happy ¹⁰ _____ work. I'm happy in my job now and I hope I can be happy in the future too.

On the Portal
Extra Practice Activities: Lesson 8.1

8.2 Grammar

Will for future predictions

GRAMMAR — Will for future predictions

+	I **will study** abroad. She **will be** a teacher. They **will have** teachers.	
–	I **won't have** homework. She **won't be** a nurse. They **won't have** coursebooks.	
?	**Will** you **study** a lot? **Will** he **play** games? **Will** they **have** teachers?	Yes, I **will**./No, I **won't**. Yes, he **will**./No, he **won't**. Yes, they **will**./No, they **won't**.
	How **will** they **learn**?	

Time expressions:
in 2040/twenty years' time/the next five years/the future
by (= before) 2040/New Year/my twentieth birthday

1 ● Complete the sentences with *will* and the verbs below.

be   break   ~~get~~   rain   win   work

1 Helena *will get* the best marks in the test. She's very clever.
2 It _____ at the weekend. I heard that on the radio.
3 In 2040 I _____ a teacher and I'll live in the countryside.
4 Be careful! You _____ the pen!
5 Our team is very good. I think they _____ the match.
6 People _____ a lot more hours in the future.

2 ● Rewrite the sentences in the negative and questions form.

1 Danny will pass the exam.
   ✗ *Danny won't pass the exam.*
   ? *Will Danny pass the exam?*
2 It will rain tomorrow.
   ✗ _____
   ? _____
3 Prices will be lower in the summer.
   ✗ _____
   ? _____
4 In the future children will start school at the age of three.
   ✗ _____
   ? _____

3 ●● Use the prompts to make sentences with *will/won't*.

1 I / not be / long
   Wait here. *I won't be long*.
2 you / help me
   _____ with this homework later?
3 it / only / take / an hour
   The journey is short. _____
4 us / teach
   I don't think Miss Jones _____ next term.
5 where / your family
   _____ live in England?
6 people / live
   _____ longer in the future.

4 ●●● Complete the text with the correct future form of the verbs in brackets.

The future of shopping

So, what [1] *will shopping be* (shopping/be) like in the future? I think we [2] _____ (do) ALL our shopping online. People [3] _____ (not need) to go out to shops. For food – our fridge [4] _____ (tell) our computers what we need. We [5] _____ (not have to) do anything! Robots [6] _____ (drive) the food to our houses. But [7] _____ (robots/choose) our clothes too? No, I don't think they [8] _____. We [9] _____ (go) online, choose our clothes and then we [10] _____ (see) a picture of ourselves in the jeans or dress on our screens and we [11] _____ (decide) to buy or not to buy! So, in the future there [12] _____ (not be) any sales assistants, just lots of robots.

20/02/2021

Unit 8 — 82 — I can use *will* to make predictions about the future.

On the Portal
Extra Practice Activities: Lesson 8.2

8.3 Reading and Vocabulary
Teenage ambitions

1 Read the article and answer the questions.
Which person chose their dream job …
- because of something they did at school? _____
- because of a present they received? _____

2 Read the text again and answer the questions.

What's your dream job?

Last month we asked you to tell us what your dream job is. Here are two of your answers.

Isabel, 14, Barcelona

What's your dream job? Why?
I'd really like to invent apps because I love gadgets and I have lots of ideas for new apps.

Describe how you decided that you want to do this.
I got my first smartphone two years ago for my birthday, and now I use it all the time. I love downloading different apps and trying them out. Also, my uncle is the boss of a small IT company, and he is helping me learn how to code. He's my role model. I have an idea for an app which helps you redesign a room, and I'd love to create it, but it's difficult!

What will you need to do?
I need to get better at coding, so I think I'll need to do a university degree in it. While I'm there I'll try and get a summer job with an IT company to get some experience. Then I'll have to create the apps I have ideas for and try to sell them. I'm not much of an entrepreneur though, so I'll need someone to help me with this.

Baris, 13, Turkey

What's your dream job? Why?
I want to be a famous actor because I really enjoy acting.

Describe how you decided that you want to do this.
At school we have drama classes, and it's my favourite subject. Last year I had the main part in the school play and I loved it. I'm also in the school drama club and we do extra classes after school. I'd love to do it as a full-time job, but I know it's difficult.

What will you need to do?
I won't need many qualifications, so I don't think I'll get a university degree. But I can do a college diploma in acting at our local college, so I'll try and do this course. I'll need to get experience working on productions and doing auditions. I think I'll have to work part-time on small productions first.

I can understand an article about teenage ambitions.

1. When did Isabel get her first smartphone?
   _____
2. What does Isabel's uncle do?
   _____
3. What does Isabel think she'll need help with?
   _____
4. What does Baris like most at school?
   _____
5. What doesn't Baris think he'll need?
   _____
6. How will he try and get experience?
   _____

3 Choose the correct answer.
1. My friend has a ___ job in the supermarket for the next six weeks, but then he'll need to find another one.
   a) temporary
   b full-time
2. You'll need a university ___ to become a teacher.
   a diploma
   b degree
3. I want to get a ___ job during July and August before I go to college.
   a full-time
   b summer
4. My aunt is a real ___. She always has lots of interesting new business ideas.
   a entrepreneur
   b boss
5. My mum had a ___ job when I was very young. She only worked a few hours every week.
   a full-time
   b part-time
6. My dad is the ___ of a small company. He has three people in his team.
   a boss
   b role model

8.4 Grammar

First Conditional

> **GRAMMAR** First Conditional
>
> - If + Present Simple, will + verb
>   If I don't do well in Science, I won't be a vet.
> - will + verb if + Present Simple
>   You won't pass your tests if you don't study.

1 **WORD FRIENDS** Choose the correct option.
1. I must learn / (revise) for my English test tomorrow.
2. Unfortunately I missed / failed my Maths test yesterday because I didn't study.
3. We're going to write / take a test next week in History.
4. We get / find the results of our tests next week.
5. I never make / get a good mark in end of term tests. I get too nervous.
6. The teacher sent Harry home because he cheated / passed in a test.

2 Put *if* in the correct position in the sentences. Add commas where necessary.
1. _If_ Dad doesn't arrive home soon _,_ his dinner will be cold.
2. _X_ We won't fail our tests _if_ we work hard.
3. ____ I'll be happy ____ I get a good mark.
4. ____ I get home too late ____ I won't call you.
5. ____ I won't go running ____ it's very cold and rainy.
6. ____ I get a summer job ____ I'll earn lots of money.
7. ____ you don't go to bed soon ____ you'll be very tired tomorrow.

3 Match the sentence halves.
1. _g_ If the bus is late,
2. ___ If my dad doesn't like his new job,
3. ___ If I don't see you after school,
4. ___ If we get good marks,
5. ___ If the jeans don't fit,
6. ___ If we win the game on Saturday,
7. ___ If you don't work hard,

a. I'll take them back to the shop tomorrow.
b. we'll be the best team in town.
c. you won't get a good job.
d. I'll see you at the party.
e. the teacher will be really pleased.
f. he'll find a different one.
g. ~~I'll miss the start of the film.~~

4 Complete the sentences with the correct form of the verbs in brackets.
1. If Dad _drives_ (drive) us to the cinema, we _'ll get_ (get) there by 4.30.
2. I _____ (not buy) any tickets if you _____ (not want) to go to the concert.
3. We _____ (be) back home before lunch if we _____ (leave) now.
4. If you _____ (go) to France in May, you _____ (have) sunny weather.
5. David _____ (have to) wear a uniform if he _____ (become) a police officer.
6. If the teacher _____ (not give) us a test tomorrow, I _____ (be) very happy.
7. _____ (you/wait?) for me if my train _____ (be) late?

5 Complete the dialogue with the correct form of the verbs below.

| ask | be | buy | give | go | not have |
| ~~miss~~ | not see | spend | | | |

A: The new clothes shop has a sale on today! Let's go after school.
B: I've got a swimming lesson after school. If I [1] _miss_ it, my teacher will be angry.
A: But if I [2] _____ without you and get some cheap boots, you [3] _____ angry!
B: If you [4] _____ any more money, you [5] _____ enough to go on holiday!
A: Ah. It's my birthday soon. If I [6] _____ my parents, they [7] _____ me money instead of a present.
B: OK! But I can't miss swimming. If I give you some money, [8] _____ you _____ me a cheap black T-shirt?
A: Yeah. If I [9] _____ any cheap ones, I'll buy you something else.
B: No, don't! Don't buy anything then!

Unit 8 84 I can use the First Conditional to talk about possible situations in the future.

On the Portal
Extra Practice Activities: Lesson 8.4

8.5 Listening and Vocabulary
A modern school

1 Complete the sentences with one word in each gap.
1. The first school I went to was a *primary* school.
2. At school we had different teachers for different subjects, but we had the same _____ tutor.
3. Chris always has lunch in the school _____.
4. In the UK, pupils finish _____ school at 16 or 18 years old.
5. You need to get good grades at school if you want to go to _____.

2 Complete the crossword. What is the hidden word?

1. c o l l e g e

1. You study here when you finish secondary school.
2. The teacher who is in charge of your school is a … teacher.
3. A young person who goes to school.
4. You study this subject in a lab.
5. You can borrow books from here.
6. A student who is in your class.
7. You use these to walk to a different level of the building.
8. A room at school where you have classes.
9. An outdoor area for children to play.

The hidden word is: _____.

3 **WORD FRIENDS** Complete the sentences with the words below.

do (x2)   give   ~~make~~   write

1. Did you *make* any notes in our History lesson today?
2. We have to _____ a long essay for English tonight.
3. If we _____ exercises 1 and 2 now, we won't need to _____ any homework tonight!
4. Tomorrow Jason is going to _____ a presentation about New York in class.

4 🔊 8.1 Listen to the radio phone-in and choose the correct answer.
1. The interviewer thinks his listeners are
   a on the school bus.
   b at home.
   c at school.
2. Monica usually has her lessons
   a in the dining room.
   b in the library.
   c in a museum.
3. Monica's mum knows what to teach because
   a she finds information on the internet.
   b a secondary school worker comes and controls her.
   c she talks to a teacher in the classroom.
4. Monica is not studying at school because
   a the classes are too big.
   b her mum is a teacher there.
   c she gets bad marks.
5. Monica would sometimes like to
   a go to a concert with friends.
   b play tennis with a friend.
   c talk about her schoolwork with a friend.

I can understand a radio interview about home-schooling.

8.6 Speaking
Expressing probability

1 🔊 **8.2** Listen and repeat the phrases.

> **SPEAKING** Expressing probability
> - I will **definitely** pass.
> - I will **probably** pass.
> - I **may/might** pass.
> - I **probably** won't pass.
> - I **definitely** won't pass.

2 Order the words in brackets to complete the sentences.

a *I will definitely go* (will/definitely/I/go) to bed early tonight.
b _____ (go/might/I) shopping tomorrow.
c _____ (won't/watch/definitely/I) the horror film.
d _____ (probably/finish/won't/I) this essay today.
e _____ (will/email/probably/I) some friends this evening.

3 Write sentences about pictures 1–7.

1 *I'll definitely learn* to play the guitar.
2 _____ lots of money.
3 _____ to drive.
4 _____ a house.
5 _____ two children.
6 _____ on safari.
7 _____ a marathon.

✓✓ – will definitely   ? – may/might   ✗✗ – definitely won't
?✓ – will probably   ?✗ – probably won't

4 🔊 **8.3** Complete the dialogue with sentences a–e. Then listen and check.

A: Hi, Beth! The Rubies are playing in town tonight at the Grange Theatre. Mike and I are going. Would you like to come too?
B: Oh, I'm not sure. ¹ *b* If I finish early, I'll come.
A: Oh, Beth. The Rubies are more important than work. ² ___ I know! I can help you with your work.
B: Brilliant! ³ ___ What time are you and Mike going?
A: ⁴ ___ I'm going to phone him in a moment to confirm. Do you want to meet us there?
B: ⁵ ___ I only get home from swimming at 7.20. How about I meet you inside at 7.45?
A: OK. Let me help you with that work now!

a I definitely won't be there by 7.30.
b ~~I might come, but I've got a lot of work.~~
c We'll probably meet outside the Grange about 7.30.
d They probably won't come to our town again for a long time.
e Then I'll definitely come!

5 Order sentences a–e from Exercise 4 (1 = most certain to happen, 5 = least certain to happen).

1 *e*   2 ☐   3 ☐   4 ☐   5 ☐

On the Portal
Extra Practice Activities: Lesson 8.6

8.7 Writing
A personal statement

1 Read the personal statement and answer the question.

What does Adam want to be in the future?
_____

Adam May

My name is Adam May and I am in the 8th grade at Boslington Middle School.

I am a very happy person. I always look at the positive side of a situation. I am also funny because I am good at making people laugh.

I am crazy about animals and I am interested in learning about animals from other countries. I am also keen on sports, especially football. I'm not brilliant at playing football though.

Last summer, I visited a city farm with my family. It was a great experience. I learned all about the animals and made new friends – pigs and chickens!

In the future, I think I'll be a vet. I really enjoy being with animals and would like to work with them full-time.

2 Read the text again and complete the notes about Adam.

- Personal qualities: ¹ *happy and funny*
- Hobbies and interests: ² _____
- Experiences: ³ _____

3 Complete the sentences with one word in each gap.
1. My name is Vicki Hopewell. I *am* fourteen years old.
2. I am friendly _____ confident.
3. It is easy _____ me to make new friends.
4. I like learning _____ languages.
5. Last year, I _____ to a summer camp.
6. In the _____, I think I'll be a doctor.

4 Choose the correct answer.
1. I'm really fond ___ animals. I'd like to be a vet.
   a at   (b) of   c in
2. I'm interested ___ learning all about the planets and space.
   a about   b on   c in
3. When my sister was young, she was crazy ___ horses.
   a at   b of   c about
4. Marsha is very keen ___ IT.
   a about   b on   c at
5. My mum is good ___ understanding how people feel.
   a of   b at   c in
6. My sister is brilliant ___ Maths.
   a at   b on   c about

WRITING TIME

5 Write a personal statement for a weekend job.

1 Find ideas
Make notes for a personal statement.
- What job would you like to have?
- What are your personal qualities, your hobbies and interests?
- What are your experiences? Talk about the skills that you can use in the job.

2 Plan and write
- Organise your ideas into paragraphs. Use Adam's personal statement to help you.
- Write a draft personal statement.

3 Check
- Check language: did you use adjectives and prepositions correctly?
- Check grammar: did you use the full forms of verbs?
- Write the final version of your personal statement.

I can write a personal statement.

My Language File

WORDLIST 🔊 8.4

Jobs
accountant (n) _____
architect (n) _____
artist (n) _____
builder (n) _____
care worker (n) _____
chef (n) _____
doctor (n) _____
driver (n) _____
engineer (n) _____
firefighter (n) _____
gardener (n) _____
hairdresser (n) _____
IT specialist (n) _____
journalist (n) _____
lawyer (n) _____
manager (n) _____
mechanic (n) _____
nurse (n) _____
pilot (n) _____
police officer (n) _____
politician (n) _____
receptionist (n) _____
scientist (n) _____
tour guide (n) _____
waiter (n) _____
waitress (n) _____

Word friends (work collocations)
be happy at work _____
earn (good) money _____
get to work on time _____
work alone _____
work as a (waitress) _____
work at the weekend _____
work for a company _____
work in a team _____
work in an office _____
work indoors _____
work outdoors _____

World of work
boss (n) _____
college diploma (n) _____
entrepreneur (n) _____
full-time job (n) _____
part-time job (n) _____
role model (n) _____
summer job (n) _____
temporary job (n) _____
university degree (n) _____

Word friends (tests)
cheat in a test _____
fail a test _____
get a bad mark _____
get a good mark _____
get the results of a test _____
have a test _____
pass a test _____
revise for a test _____
study for a test _____
take a test _____

School and education
canteen (n) _____
classmate (n) _____
classroom (n) _____
college (n) _____
computer room (n) _____
English teacher (n) _____
form tutor (n) _____
head teacher (n) _____
library (n) _____
Maths teacher (n) _____
playground (n) _____
primary school (n) _____
pupil (n) _____
Science lab (n) _____
secondary school (n) _____
sports hall (n) _____
staff room (n) _____
stairs (n) _____
university (n) _____

Word friends (schoolwork)
do exercises _____
do your homework _____
give presentations _____
make notes _____
write essays _____

Extra words
babysitter (n) _____
bike courier (n) _____
brilliant at (adj) _____
business (n) _____
communication skills (n) _____
crazy about (adj) _____
dog walker (n) _____
exam (n) _____
fond of (adj) _____
fruit picker (n) _____
future career (n) _____
good at (adj) _____
interests (n) _____
keen on (adj) _____
learn (v) _____
lesson (n) _____
lifeguard (n) _____
machine (n) _____
museum guide (n) _____
(not) bad at (adj) _____
personal qualities (n) _____
personal statement (n) _____
revision plan (n) _____
stressful (adj) _____
timetable (n) _____
workmate (n) _____

Sounds good!
Fingers crossed! _____
What a nightmare! _____
You'll be in trouble. _____

MY LANGUAGE NOTES

My favourite words/expressions from this unit

Self-check

Vocabulary

1 Complete the sentences with the correct jobs.
1. Ian is a _____ who writes articles.
2. My aunt's a _____ for old people in a care home.
3. I don't want to be an _____ because I don't like working with numbers.
4. My friend loves planting and looking after trees and plants. He wants to be a _____.
5. My brother is training to be an _____. He wants to design eco-friendly buildings.
6. Kevin knows a lot about ancient sites – he's a _____.

2 Choose the correct option.
1. Some people don't want to work *in / for* a company, and start their own business.
2. It's important to work *at / in* a team if you want to get results.
3. Tony worked *as / like* a postman for two months.
4. Jim is really bad at getting to work *on / in* time.
5. It's great to *win / earn* a lot of money, but it's more important to be happy at work.
6. Dan doesn't like his job because he works *as / in* an office all day.
7. I'm really interested *for / in* learning more about jobs like this.
8. Richard is looking *at / for* a summer job this year.

3 Complete the sentences with the words below.

> classmates   head   library   playground
> pupils   staff

1. My primary school was very small and it only had sixty _____.
2. I'd like to speak to Miss Turner. Is she in the _____ room?
3. The class teacher sent Tom to see the _____ teacher because he was fighting in class.
4. The children play games in the _____.
5. I work in the _____ because it's quiet.
6. I get on well with all my _____. We're good friends.

Grammar

4 Complete the sentences with *will* and the verbs in brackets.
1. In the future there _____ (not be) any TVs. We _____ (watch) films and programmes on computers.
2. _____ (you/stay) at a hotel in Spain when you're on holiday next week?
3. After university I _____ (not get) a job. I _____ (be) a traveller for a few months.
4. Jan _____ (be) seventeen next Sunday. She _____ (be able) to learn to drive!
5. _____ (you/be) at home this evening? I _____ (phone) you at about 7.30.
6. The test tomorrow _____ (not finish) before 12.15.

5 Choose the correct option.
1. *Does / Will* your brother take his driving test again if he fails it tomorrow?
2. If I *go / will go* to bed late, I will be tired.
3. We'll move if my dad *gets / will get* a new job.
4. Where *do you / will you* go swimming if they close the Sports Centre?
5. If I *don't / won't* get good marks, I won't be happy!

Speaking

6 Order the words in brackets to complete the sentences.
1. Look at the time! _____ (be/will/definitely/we) late.
2. _____ (probably/won't/I) see you tomorrow. Good luck with the exam!
3. Don't leave yet. _____ (arrive/they/might) soon.
4. _____ (you/come/definitely/will) to the party? It will be good to see you.
5. Sophie doesn't eat a lot. _____ (want/might/she/not) a big meal.

YOUR SCORE

Vocabulary: __/20   Speaking: __/5
Grammar: __/15   Total: __/40

It's only natural

9

VOCABULARY
Geographical features | *In, on, by* |
Talking about countries | Phrasal verbs |
Outdoor activities | Sporting equipment

GRAMMAR
Present Perfect | Present Perfect with *just, already* and *yet*

9.1 Vocabulary
Landscapes

1 Look at photos 1–8 and complete the names of the geographical features.

1 b _e_ _a_ _c_ _h_
2 c _ _ _ _ _
3 l _ _ _
4 r _ _ _ _ _
5 f _ _ _ _ _ _
6 i _ _ _ _ _
7 h _ _ _
8 s _ _

2 Complete the crossword.

Across
3 an area of land with lots of tropical plants and trees
4 a forest with tall trees, warm climate and lots of rain
6 a very big sea
8 where a river falls over a cliff
9 a hot and dry area with no plants

Down
1 a very high hill
2 a low area between high hills
5 an area of grass where farmers can keep animals
7 this is where the land meets the sea

3 j u n g l e

3 Read the notices. Then complete the labels with the words below.

a beach   a cliff   a desert   a field
a mountain   a rainforest   a river

Check the **WEATHER FORECAST** before starting to climb.

1 _a mountain_

USE THE BRIDGE TO CROSS
– 300 metres away.

2 _____

NO WATER
for the next 50 km.

3 _____

Sun chairs here **50p** an hour.

4 _____

NO CLIMBING.
Danger – falling rocks.

5 _____

Help the environment
– *save the trees!*

6 _____

PUBLIC PATH
but please shut the gate – farm animals.

7 _____

Unit 9   90

4 Match notices 1–7 from Exercise 3 with meanings a–g below.

a [7] You can walk across here, but be careful.
b [ ] You don't have to lie on the sand.
c [ ] You mustn't do this – it's dangerous.
d [ ] Weather change can make this place dangerous.
e [ ] We need to think about the future.
f [ ] Take something to drink with you.
g [ ] You need to walk a short way to find something.

5 **WORD FRIENDS** Choose the correct option.

1 We had a great skiing holiday (in)/ on the mountains last month.
2 On our walk we saw some black cows on / in a big field.
3 My uncle has a house by / on a lake and it's very beautiful there.
4 My parents would like to live in / on the coast so they can look at the sea every day.
5 My friend lives in / on an island and has to take a boat to go to school every morning.
6 We can walk along this path and then have a picnic by / in the river.

6 Choose the correct answer.

1 I live about 100 kilometres from England's ___ city, London.
   a official   (b) capital   c national
2 I live in a small town in Italy near the ___ with France.
   a population   b coast   c border
3 Our house is in a village where the ___ is only 540!
   a population   b country   c border
4 The ___ of my country has two colours: red and white.
   a official language   b island   c flag
5 The ___ language of my country is French, but people speak other languages, too.
   a flag   b capital   c official

7 Choose the correct option.

If you're looking for somewhere to spend a holiday in a quiet part of the UK, then come to the New Forest! Only a two-hour drive from the ¹*official language /(capital city)* of England, it is located in the beautiful county of Hampshire, on the ²*coast / border* with Dorset. It is one of the most beautiful areas in the country, and is very quiet, with a ³*population / language* of under 200,000. If you stay in a hotel in a New Forest village, you can go on trips to the ⁴*coast / desert* and visit such beautiful cities as Winchester and Salisbury. If you like walking, then the New Forest is the place for you! You can look at different types of trees, follow small ⁵*lakes / rivers* and see the famous New Forest ponies. They are free to walk anywhere, even on the roads, and don't live in ⁶*islands / fields*. So be careful if you're driving, a pony could walk right in front of you! If you go to the ⁷*rainforest / sea* you can walk along the ⁸*beaches / jungle* and look across the water to some pretty ⁹*flags / islands*. The ¹⁰*cliffs / desert* along the beaches are high and can be dangerous, so don't walk too close to them. Interested in the New Forest?
Check out our website …

I can talk about landscapes and nature.

9.2 Grammar

Present Perfect

> **GRAMMAR** — **Present Perfect**
>
> **+** I've (have) swum with dolphins.
> He's (has) visited 150 countries.
> They've (have) learned a lot.
>
> **−** I haven't visited Africa.
> She hasn't finished the trip.
> They haven't had problems.
>
> **?** Have you learned a lot? | Yes, I have./No, I haven't.
> Has he enjoyed Thailand? | Yes, he has./No, he hasn't.
> Have they finished? | Yes, they have./No, they haven't.
>
> Which countries have you enjoyed most?

1 ● Complete the sentences with the affirmative Present Perfect form of the verbs below.

| eat | play | see | ~~sleep~~ | win | write |

1 I *have slept* in a tent.
2 My brother _____ two short stories.
3 My mother _____ Mexican food.
4 My cousins _____ basketball in the USA.
5 You _____ lots of medals.
6 Danny _____ the Eiffel Tower.

2 ●● Order the words in brackets to complete the sentences.

1 *I've never been* (been/I've/never) to Italy.
2 Have _____ (you/ever/eaten) fruit salad?
3 Our teacher _____ (never/forgotten/has) to mark our homework.
4 _____ (seen/we/haven't) the new sci-fi film.
5 My brother _____ (never/played/has/football).
6 _____ (computer/has/ever/your) crashed?
7 How many times _____ (been/have/France/you/to)?

3 ●● Complete the sentences with the correct Present Perfect form of the verbs in brackets.

1 *Have you ever met* (you/ever/meet) anyone famous?
2 I _____ (never fly) in a helicopter.
3 Erin _____ (not see) our new car.
4 How many people _____ (you/invite) to your party?
5 We _____ (not study) the Present Perfect before.
6 _____ (your parents/ever/live) in another country?
7 Which countries _____ (you/visit)?
8 I _____ (never eat) sushi.

4 ●●● Complete the dialogue with the correct form of the verbs in brackets.

A: So, you'd like to be a tour guide for our company. ¹*Have you been* (you/be) to many countries?
B: Yes. I ² _____ (travel) a lot. I ³ _____ (be) to most European countries on holiday and I ⁴ _____ (visit) the United States.
A: ⁵ _____ (you/ever/give) talks or presentations about famous sights?
B: Yes, ⁶ _____ (do) quite a lot! I'm really interested in museums and important buildings. I ⁷ _____ (also/do) some projects about famous art galleries in the world.
A: Excellent. What other experience do you have that's important for a tour guide?
B: Well, I ⁸ _____ (learn) three languages and passed exams in all three. So, I now speak French, Chinese and Russian. I think that will help.
A: Oh, yes.
B: And I ⁹ _____ (make) lots of friends in different countries, so I know quite a lot about different cultures.
A: Very good. I think you'll be very good at the job!

Unit 9 — 92 — I can use the Present Perfect to talk about experiences.

On the Portal
Extra Practice Activities: Lesson 9.2

9.3 Reading and Vocabulary
Exploring nature

1 Read the article and answer the question.
Which countries does it mention?
_____

Cameron Davis, the teenage boy who's seen the world

Imagine you're thirteen years old and you've visited forty-five countries. You've seen many wonders of the world and you have tried lots of new experiences. This is life for Cameron Davis!

When Cameron was just five years old, his family took him to Peru. They enjoyed the trip so much that they decided to take up travelling and carry on visiting new places. The next year, they visited twenty-nine countries.

Cameron has learned a lot on his travels. He says that before they travelled he used to be shy. But after travelling and meeting new people and having new experiences, he's now much more confident and sociable. But it wasn't always easy. Once when he was in Vietnam he was playing with another boy who bit him! He thought that maybe he should give up and go back to being shy, but he didn't. And now he even has his own YouTube channel.

On his travels, he's tried a lot of new things too. He's been mountain biking in Canada, cooked pad thai in Thailand, eaten curries in India and tried dumplings in China.

He's also learned how to become more independent. For example, he now packs his own suitcase before he travels, and helps his parents at home. He says he's come across lots of families in which everyone depends on each other.

What advice does Cameron have for other teenagers? Talk more, take risks and try new things.

2 Read the text again and tick (✓) four things Cameron has tried.
1 ☐ mountain biking
2 ☐ surfing
3 ☐ cooking
4 ☐ trying new foods
5 ☐ snowboarding
6 ☐ packing his own suitcase

3 Read the text again and complete the notes with a word or short phrase.

1 Number of countries visited at age 13: 45
2 Age when Cameron visited 29 countries: _____
3 What he didn't stop doing after an incident in Vietnam: _____
4 Cameron's personality now: _____
5 Types of food he's tried: _____
6 What he's learned to be after travelling: _____

4 **WORD FRIENDS** Choose the correct answer.
1 I know you're tired, but don't give ____. Keep running!
   a on   (b) up   c over
2 It's too difficult to get there. Let's just go ____.
   a back   b across   c up
3 What famous places did you come ____ while you were travelling?
   a over   b out   c across
4 I know it's difficult, but let's carry ____ a bit longer.
   a on   b up   c back
5 I'd like to take ____ a new sport this year.
   a in   b up   c out

I can understand an article about a teenage explorer.

9.4 Grammar

Present Perfect with *just*, *already* and *yet*

GRAMMAR — Present Perfect with *just*, *already* and *yet*

+	He's **just** sent a text. I've **already** sent two texts.
–	He hasn't replied **yet**.
?	Have you texted him **yet**?	Yes, I have./No, I haven't.

1 ● Put the words in brackets in the correct positions in the sentences.
1. I've finished cleaning the house. (just)
   I've just finished cleaning the house.
2. I've read that book. (already)
   _____
3. We haven't studied the grammar. (yet)
   _____
4. Mick has phoned. (just)
   _____
5. Has the teacher marked our homework? (yet)
   _____
6. I haven't been to the beach. (yet)
   _____

2 ●● Match the sentences in Exercise 1 with sentences a–f below.
- a [4] He can't go swimming with us.
- b [ ] I'm really tired.
- c [ ] Is it sandy?
- d [ ] Have you got another one?
- e [ ] We gave it to her a week ago.
- f [ ] We can't do this exercise.

3 ●● Order the words in brackets to complete the sentences.
1. *Have you been to* (to/have/been/you) the new exhibition yet?
2. Dad _____ (just/booked/has) our holiday in Spain.
3. I _____ (to/yet/spoken/haven't) Bill about the concert _____.
4. _____ (seen/already/have/we) that film.
5. _____ (just/I've/opened) your email.
6. _____ (she/invited/already/has) you to the party?

4 ●● Rewrite the sentences using *already*, *just* or *yet*.
1. I spoke to Pat a few moments ago.
   I've just spoken to Pat.
2. I did my homework earlier this morning.
   _____
3. I need to tidy my room.
   _____
4. Did you clean the car this morning?
   _____
5. My friend sent me a really funny video clip about five minutes ago.
   _____
6. We went to the museum yesterday.
   _____

5 ●●● Choose the correct answer.

Hello from Barbados!

I've ¹_____ been on a holiday like this before. It's wonderful. We arrived two hours ago, but we've ²_____ been to the beach and it's amazing. Have you ever ³_____ a photo of a Caribbean beach? It's lovely white sand and the sea is a beautiful blue! And I ⁴_____ never felt so hot before – but not uncomfortable. I've ⁵_____ swimming and my back ⁶_____ already gone brown! I've met some really nice people and we're going to have a meal with them tonight. OK, must stop now because Dad has ⁷_____ called me. We're going back to the hotel. We haven't unpacked ⁸_____!

	a	b	c
1	ever	**(b) never**	sometimes
2	yet	already	ever
3	see	saw	seen
4	have	haven't	had
5	go	been	was
6	have	has	haven't
7	already	yet	just
8	ever	just	yet

Unit 9 | 94 | I can use the Present Perfect to talk about recent events.

On the Portal
Extra Practice Activities: Lesson 9.4

9.5 Listening and Vocabulary
Outdoor activities

1 Complete the table with the words below.

~~cycling~~   hiking   horse-riding   kayaking
mountain biking   rock climbing   sailing
scuba diving   skiing   snowboarding
surfing   swimming   windsurfing

Land sports	Water sports
cycling	

2 Complete the sentences with the words below.

~~biking~~   rock   scuba   skiing
swimming   windsurfing

1 We often go mountain *biking*.
2 I'm going _____ diving in Egypt soon.
3 I'd love to go _____ climbing, but it's quite dangerous.
4 I once went _____, but I kept falling into the water!
5 I went _____ in a lake with my dad last week. It was fun!
6 Every winter we go _____ in the Alps.

3 Write the words for the definitions.

1 You wear this on your head for protection.
   h *e l m e t*
2 You use this to find your way when you are mountain biking. c_ _ _ _ _ _ _
3 You wear this to keep warm in water.
   w_ _ _ _ _ _
4 You use this long thing to move a boat through water. p_ _ _ _ _ _
5 You wear these on your hands for protection.
   g_ _ _ _ _ _
6 You wear these to protect your eyes.
   g_ _ _ _ _ _ _
7 You ride this in the waves.
   s_ _ _ _ _ _ _ _

4 Choose the correct option.

1 You need to wear good (**boots**)/ gloves on your feet when you're climbing.
2 My friend has a brilliant *surfboard / snowboard*. She can go down the mountain really fast on it.
3 Before you get in the boat make sure you're wearing a *life jacket / wetsuit*.
4 This *paddle / kayak* is very light. You can go down the river very fast when you're in it.
5 I think we might be lost. Let's have a look at the *goggles / compass*.
6 Is that a road *bike / kayak*, or can you ride it in the mountains too?
7 I can't ride a horse without a *saddle / paddle*.
8 She was travelling by *map / boat*.

5 🔊 9.1 Listen to Adam talking to Emily about his family and the sports they do. Match people 1–5 and sports a–h they do NOW. There are three extra sports.

People
1 ☐ Adam
2 ☐ his cousin Ken
3 ☐ his sister
4 ☐ his dad
5 ☐ his brother

Sports
a scuba diving
b swimming
c skiing
d kayaking
e sailing
f mountain climbing
g snowboarding
h windsurfing

I can understand people talking about outdoor activities.

9.6 Speaking
Asking for, giving and refusing permission

1 🔊 9.2 Listen and repeat the phrases.

> **SPEAKING** — Asking for, giving and refusing permission
>
> **Asking for permission**
> Can I/we have a look at the map?
> Do you mind if I/we borrow your suncream?
> Is it OK/all right (for me/us) to use your tablet?
> Is it OK/all right if I/we use your dictionary?
>
> **Giving permission**
> Yes, of course.   No problem.   Sure, go ahead.
>
> **Refusing permission**
> Sorry/I'm sorry, but you can't.
> I'm afraid that's not possible.
> I'm afraid that's not a good idea.

2 Choose the correct option.
1. Is *there / it* all right for me to walk through this field?
2. Sure – go *ahead / forward*.
3. *Can / Is* it OK for my brother borrow your life jacket?
4. Do you mind *if / of* I use your map?
5. I'm *frightened / afraid* it's not possible.
6. I'm sorry, but you *couldn't / can't* use your phone here.
7. No *problem / worry*. That's fine.

3 Mark the sentences from Exercise 1 AFP (asking for permission), GP (giving permission) or RP (refusing permission).

1 *AFP*   5 _____
2 _____   6 _____
3 _____   7 _____
4 _____

4 Order the sentences to make dialogues.

1 a ☐ No problem.
   b ☐ Thanks. That's great.
   c ☐ 1 Do you mind if I use the car later?

2 a ☐ I'm afraid that's not possible. The boat's too small.
   b ☐ Is it all right for my brother to come too?
   c ☐ That's OK. He can stay on the beach.

3 a ☐ I'm sorry, but you can't. I'm using them la
   b ☐ Sure, go ahead.
   c ☐ Can we borrow your skis this morning?
   d ☐ Can I ask you a favour?

5 🔊 9.3 Complete the dialogue with sentences a–h. Then listen and check.

Steve: Oh, Tom, I like this hotel room. It will be good to share. ¹ *h*
Tom: No problem, Steve. ² ___
Steve: That's good. And there are two wardrobes. ³ ___
Tom: Sure, go ahead. ⁴ ___ Mine is a bit small.
Steve: ⁵ ___ Oh, here's Kerry. Hiya! What's your room like, Kerry?
Kerry: It's cool. Great view! But my wardrobe's really small. ⁶ ___
Steve: ⁷ ___ We've already filled ours up.
Kerry: That's OK. I'll ask Mum and Dad.
Steve: Good idea. Right, I'm going to have a shower before we go to the restaurant.
Tom: ⁸ ___ I'd like one now too.
Kerry: Sorry, Tom, but you can't. I'm in it! Bye!

a Can I have this one?
b Is it all right for me to put some of my dresses in yours?
c I'm afraid that's not possible.
d Yes, of course – there's lots of room.
e I don't mind sleeping by the door.
f Is it all right to put my jacket in yours?
g Kerry, is it OK for me to use the shower in your room?
h ~~Is it OK for me to have the bed by the window?~~

Unit 9 | 96 | I can ask for, give and refuse permission.

On the Portal
Extra Practice Activities: Lesson 9.6

9.7 Writing

An informal email about a holiday

1 Complete the sentences with the verbs below.

| ~~been~~ (x2) | had (x2) | made | sunbathed | visited |
| watched |

1. I've *been* to a souvenir shop.
2. We _____ on the beach all morning.
3. Mum and Dad _____ a museum yesterday.
4. We've _____ some lovely walks.
5. Jack and I have _____ the sunset. It was beautiful.
6. We _____ a barbecue on the beach on Saturday.
7. I've _____ friends with lots of people my own age.
8. We've all _____ to the cinema to see the new James Bond film.

2 Choose the correct option.

Hi Joe!

¹(Here) / There we are in Bournemouth.
²We're having / We have a great time and the weather has ³had / been amazing. It's been sunny and hot every day. We're staying at a top hotel – it's the best place I've ever ⁴lived / stayed at! We've been ⁵at / to lots of nice places and Fran's bought loads of souvenirs! Tomorrow I ⁶'m going / go windsurfing. That's going to be fun! I think I'm going to fall off the board a lot!

⁷See / Seeing you soon.

Lots of love,
Ellie

⁸PS / SP: I've met a lot of great people! :)
Tell you all about them next week!

---

3 Match functions 1–5 with sentences a–e. Then add another sentence for each function from Ellie's message.

1. [d] Say where you are:
   Here we are in Bournemouth.
2. [ ] Describe the weather:
   _____
3. [ ] Say what you've done:
   _____
4. [ ] Talk about your plans:
   _____
5. [ ] Ending:
   _____

a. It's been windy all week.
b. Miss you!
c. We've had lots of walks.
d. ~~I'm writing from my hotel room.~~
e. We're coming home on Monday.

4 Complete the table with the synonyms below.

| ~~amazing~~ | awful | brilliant | dull | exhausted | great |
| lovely | sleepy | terrible |

good	bad	boring	tired
amazing	_____	_____	_____
_____	_____	_____	_____
_____	_____	_____	_____

WRITING TIME

5 Imagine you are on holiday. Write an email to your friend.

1 Find ideas
Make notes about:
- the place and the weather.
- what you have done so far.
- your plans.

2 Plan and write
- Organise your ideas into paragraphs. Use Ellie's message to help you.
- Write a draft informal email.

3 Check
- Check language: are the adjective synonyms correct?
- Check grammar: are the Present Perfect verbs correct?
- Write the final version of your informal email.

I can write an informal email about a holiday.

My Language File

WORDLIST 🔊 9.4

Geographical features
- beach (n) _____
- cliff (n) _____
- coast (n) _____
- desert (n) _____
- field (n) _____
- forest (n) _____
- hill (n) _____
- island (n) _____
- jungle (n) _____
- lake (n) _____
- mountain (n) _____
- ocean (n) _____
- rainforest (n) _____
- river (n) _____
- sea (n) _____
- valley (n) _____
- waterfall (n) _____

Word friends (in, on, by)
- by a lake _____
- by a river _____
- by the sea _____
- in a field _____
- in a forest _____
- in a lake _____
- in a valley _____
- in the mountains _____
- in the sea _____
- on a beach _____
- on a hill _____
- on a mountain _____
- on an island _____
- on the coast _____

Talking about countries
- border (n) _____
- capital city (n) _____
- flag (n) _____
- official language (n) _____
- population (n) _____

Word friends (phrasal verbs)
- carry on (v) _____
- come across (v) _____
- give up (v) _____
- go back (v) _____
- take up (v) _____

Outdoor activities
- cycling (n) _____
- hiking (n) _____
- horse-riding (n) _____
- kayaking (n) _____
- mountain biking (n) _____
- rock climbing (n) _____
- sailing (n) _____
- scuba diving (n) _____
- skiing (n) _____
- snowboarding (n) _____
- surfing (n) _____
- swimming (n) _____
- windsurfing (n) _____

Sporting equipment
- bike (n) _____
- boat (n) _____
- boots (n) _____
- compass (n) _____
- gloves (n) _____
- goggles (n) _____
- helmet (n) _____
- kayak (n) _____
- life jacket (n) _____
- map (n) _____
- paddle (n) _____
- saddle (n) _____
- snowboard (n) _____
- surfboard (n) _____
- wetsuit (n) _____

Extra words
- amazing (adj) _____
- barbecue (n) _____
- bridge (n) _____
- camp (v) _____
- climate change (n) _____
- climb (v) _____
- dry (adj) _____
- dull (adj) _____
- equipment (n) _____
- exhausted (adj) _____
- experience (n) _____
- freezing (adj) _____
- get lost _____
- hang out with _____
- heavy (adj) _____
- high (adj) _____
- holiday (n) _____
- ice cap (n) _____
- instructor (n) _____
- irritating (adj) _____
- kilometre (n) _____
- land (n) _____
- leader (n) _____
- low (adj) _____
- path (n) _____
- reach the top _____
- rest (n) _____
- scared (adj) _____
- share a border _____
- ski (v) _____
- ski boots (n) _____
- ski poles (n) _____
- skis (n) _____
- sled (n) _____
- souvenir (n) _____
- spectacular (adj) _____
- sun cream (n) _____
- sunbathe (v) _____
- sunset (n) _____
- travel (v) _____
- trip (n) _____
- visa (n) _____
- wet (adj) _____

Sounds good!
- Thank goodness! _____
- I'm starving! _____
- It's not cool. _____

MY LANGUAGE NOTES

My favourite words/expressions from this unit

_____   _____
_____   _____
_____   _____
_____   _____

Self-check

Vocabulary

1 Choose the correct option.
1. On Sunday afternoon we sunbathed on the *coast / beach*.
2. We swam across the small *waterfall / river* and walked in the *fields / cliffs*.
3. We went round the *hill / island* in a boat.
4. What's the capital *language / city* of your country?
5. It can be very dangerous to climb up a *mountain / jungle* alone.
6. The *flag / border* of my country is blue and white.
7. She loves swimming in the *desert / lake* near her home.

2 Complete the sentences with the words below.

> climbing   cycling   scuba diving   snowboarding
> surfing   swimming   windsurfing

1. Young people often go _____ in the park near our home.
2. My brother usually goes _____ and takes photos of fish.
3. I hope it's windy tomorrow, so I can go _____.
4. I'm not very good at skiing in the snow, but I love _____.
5. We can't go _____ today because there's no wind!
6. My dad goes rock _____ in the mountains every year.
7. I love _____ in a pool but not in a river or lake.

3 Complete the words in the sentences.
1. You should always wear a l___ j_____ when you're in a boat to keep safe.
2. We went down the river in a k_____.
3. Oh, no! I lost a p_____ in the water! How are we going to get back to the beach?
4. Don't go cycling without your h_____. It's dangerous. You might hurt your head.
5. I always wear g_____ when I'm skiing to protect my eyes from the sun and snow.
6. You can see on the m___ that we're near a forest.

Grammar

4 Complete the sentences with the Present Perfect form of the verbs in brackets.
1. I _____ never _____ (forget) to do my English homework.
2. My mum _____ already _____ (write) ten emails this morning!
3. Jack and Pete _____ already _____ (see) this film five times.
4. My brother _____ already _____ (drink) all the milk.
5. I'm afraid Helen _____ already _____ (leave) the office.
6. I _____ never _____ (buy) plastic shoes.
7. _____ you _____ (do) your homework yet?
8. They _____ just _____ (arrive) home.

5 Complete the sentences with the correct form of the Present Perfect.
1. _____ (you/see) the new show yet?
2. We _____ (not have) dinner yet.
3. I _____ (just/speak) to Lee about Ben.
4. Tom _____ (already/buy) our train tickets.
5. _____ (you/ever/work) in France?
6. Lara and Dan _____ (never/be) camping.
7. _____ (you/ever/see) that film?

Speaking

6 Complete the dialogues with one word in each gap.
1. A: _____ I use your goggles please?
   B: Yes, of _____ you can.
2. A: Is it all right _____ me to leave my bike here?
   B: Sure, _____ ahead.
3. A: Do you _____ if I borrow this wetsuit?
   B: No problem.

YOUR SCORE

Vocabulary: __/20   Speaking: __/5
Grammar: __/15   Total: __/40

Reading Time 3

Round the World in Eighty Days

Can Phileas Fogg go round the world in eighty days? He doesn't know that somebody wants to stop him. Then Fogg will lose his bet, twenty thousand pounds!

Phileas Fogg was captain of the ship. Captain Speedy was in his room, and two seamen watched him carefully. He couldn't leave the room. He shouted, but he couldn't get out.

What happened on that day was this: Phileas Fogg wanted to go to Liverpool. The captain didn't want to go there, but the seamen hated their captain. And Phileas Fogg gave them some money, so they were happy about the new plan.

Now the captain had to stay in his room. Aouda was not very happy about it, but Passepartout enjoyed it.

Phileas Fogg was a very good ship's captain. Perhaps he was a seaman when he was younger. With her fast engine, and the wind behind her, the *Henrietta* moved quickly over the water.

But one of the seamen said, 'Mr Fogg, this engine can take us faster. We have to put more wood on the fire.'

'And where do we get more wood?'

'From the ship. They built everything on it from wood.'

'Thank you,' said Phileas Fogg. 'I'll have to think about it.' He walked round the ship looking at the wood. Then he called Passepartout. 'Bring Captain Speedy to me.'

Captain Speedy ran to Phileas Fogg. He wanted to kill him.

'Thief!' he shouted. 'You took my ship! Where are we?'

'Seven hundred and seventy miles from Liverpool,' said Fogg. 'But I sent for you, Captain, because I want to buy your ship.'

'No! No! No!'

'I'm going to put some of it on the fire, so the engine can take us to Liverpool faster.'

'My ship! This ship cost fifty thousand dollars!'

'Here's sixty thousand,' said Phileas Fogg, and he gave the captain the money. Twelve thousand pounds.

'Oh!' Captain Speedy was suddenly a different man. The *Henrietta* cost fifty thousand dollars, but she was twenty years old.

'You, er … You only want the wood. I'll have the engine, the …'

'Oh yes. I'm only buying the wood.'

'Thank you,' said the captain.

And so, at 11.40 on 21 December, Phileas Fogg put his foot on the ground in Liverpool. And at 11.41, Fix said, 'Phileas Fogg, I'm a Scotland Yard detective. Please come with me to the nearest police station.'

Before you read

1 Match sentences 1–4 with pictures A–D.
1. Mr Barnes is captain of the ship.
2. The thief couldn't get out of the room.
3. The wind moves the ship, but it also has an engine.
4. Put some more wood on the fire.

A ☐ B ☐ C ☐ D ☐

2 Read the summary of the story and look at the book cover. Then choose the correct option.

> Phileas Fogg is a rich man in London who has a new servant called Jean Passepartout. Every day Fogg meets his friends at a club, and one day they make a bet. Fogg wants to travel round the world in 80 days, but his friends think he can't do it. So, they bet him twenty thousand pounds that he can't. Fogg and Passepartout travel from London to Egypt, then to India, where they rescue a woman, Aouda, from her village. They then travel to Hong Kong and to Japan. Next, they sail across the Pacific Ocean to San Francisco and across America. On the way a police detective follows them because he thinks Fogg is a bank thief trying to escape, but he can't arrest Fogg until he arrives back in England.

1. Phileas Fogg lives in London with *Aouda / Passepartout*.
2. His friends think it's *possible / impossible* to travel round the world in 80 days.
3. The bet is for *£10,000 / £20,000*.
4. They meet Aouda in *Hong Kong / India*.
5. The detective thinks Fogg is a *captain / thief*.

While you read

3 🔊 RT3.1 Read and listen to the story. Number events a–f in the order that they happen.
a ☐ The old captain is locked in his room.
b ☐ They arrive in England.
c ☐ One of the seamen suggests they use the ship's engine.
d ☐ Phileas Fogg becomes captain of the ship.
e ☐ The detective arrests Fogg.
f ☐ Fogg buys the boat from the old captain.

4 Read the story again. Choose the correct option.
1. *Passepartout / Aouda* was happy when the captain was locked in his room.
2. They can get wood for the fire from *their supplies / the ship*.
3. Fogg pays *twelve / sixty* thousand dollars for the ship.
4. They reach Liverpool in the *morning / afternoon*.

After you read

5 Write the Past Simple form of the verbs from the story.
1. say _____
2. build _____
3. run _____
4. give _____
5. cost _____
6. put _____

6 Match sentences a–d with their meanings 1–4.
a ☐ I watched him carefully.
b ☐ I was suddenly a different man or woman.
c ☐ I put my foot on the ground.
d ☐ I put some of it on the fire.

1. I left a boat or plane and walked on land.
2. I paid attention to someone's action very closely.
3. I made something catch fire on purpose.
4. I changed character very quickly.

7 **WRAP UP** Complete the information about the story.

> Title: _____
> Type: *adventure story / love story / crime story*
> Main characters: _____
> _____
> Important object: _____
> My opinion: ☆☆☆☆☆

101 Unit 9

Exam Time 1 — Listening — Units 1–3

1 🔊 **ET1–3.1** Listen and choose the correct answer.

> **Exam tip**
> Look at the pictures before you listen and try to name what they show.

1 Which film do they want to see?
A ☐   B ☐   C ☐

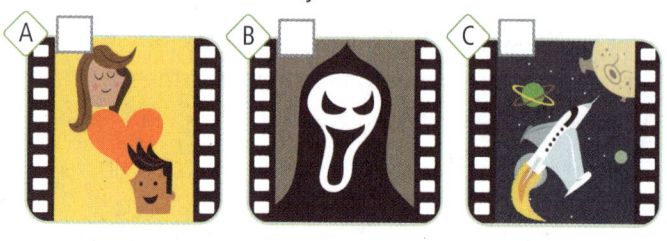

2 What does the boy's uncle do?
A ☐   B ☐   C ☐

3 What does the girl decide to wear for the party?
A ☐   B ☐   C ☐

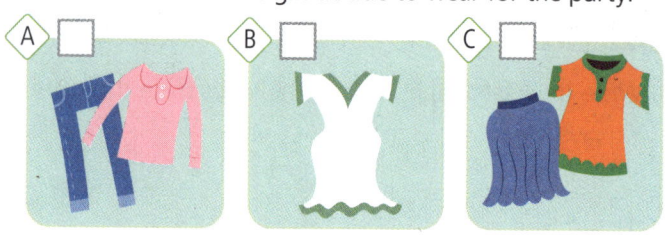

4 Which pets has the girl got?
A ☐   B ☐   C ☐

5 When is Tina's birthday?
A ☐ Thursday   B ☐ Friday   C ☐ Saturday

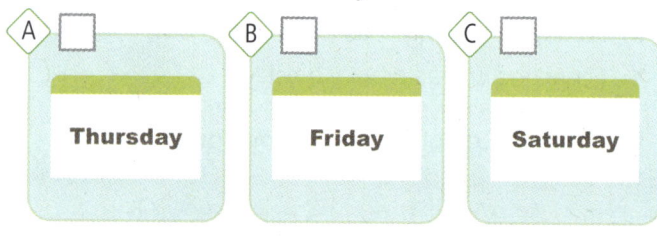

6 How many students are in the girl's class?
A ☐ 21   B ☐ 23   C ☐ 28

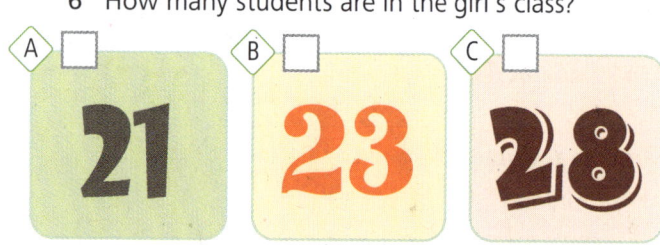

2 🔊 **ET1–3.2** Listen. Then listen again and write down what you hear during each pause.

> **Exam tip**
> Don't panic if you can't hear a word. Leave a space and keep writing.

3 🔊 **ET1–3.3** Listen to Alex talking to his friend Lindsay about his new hobby. Choose the correct answer.

1 Which free time activity doesn't Alex do anymore?
  a play football   b play the guitar
  c do salsa

2 Which language is he learning?
  a Italian   b French
  c Spanish

3 How is he learning it?
  a online   b at school
  c with his dad

4 How long are his lessons?
  a forty minutes   b forty-five minutes
  c fifty minutes

5 What is hard for him?
  a the grammar   b the vocabulary
  c the writing

6 What time is Lindsay's swimming lesson?
  a 4.30 p.m.   b 4.50 p.m.
  c 5.15 p.m.

4 🔊 **ET1–3.4** Listen to a girl, Fran, asking a friend about helping at an animal centre. Complete the notes with the missing information.

Animal Centre with Fran

When: ¹*after school today*
Work this week: ² _____
Transport: ³ Fran by _____
            ⁴ Oliver by _____
Address: ⁵ _____
Fran's number: ⁶ _____
Wear: ⁷ _____

Exam Time 1 — Reading and Writing — Units 1–3

5 Read the texts and choose the correct answer.

Farm Stay Holidays

Come to stay on our farm and enjoy life with the animals.
You can help milk the cows and feed the sheep.
We'd like to have some donkeys soon.
You can buy local fruit, vegetables and milk from the farm, but we don't have any eggs this year.

1 Which picture shows the farm?

A ☐ B ☐ C ☐

Last night I went to see **GOT TO DANCE**. I'm not really into ballroom dancing. I prefer street dance, but I thought this dance show was really exciting. It was more interesting than the ballet show I saw last month!

2 Which type of show is Got to Dance?

A ☐ B ☐ C ☐

At the weekend, we went to the town centre on the train. We wanted to go to the theatre, but the tickets were too expensive, so we went to the museum. It was cool! We were there for so long we didn't have enough time to go shopping!

3 What did the writer do at the weekend?

A ☐ B ☐ C ☐

Hi Mum, are you going to the shopping centre today? Can you look for some dark blue jeans for me? I don't want them to be too tight, but not baggy like my black ones. Thanks, Esme

4 What type of jeans does Esme want?

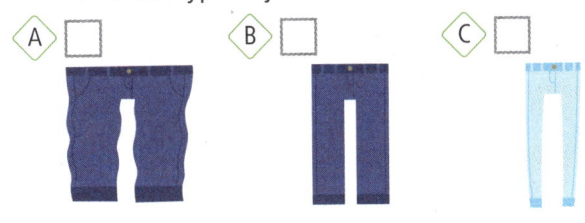

A ☐ B ☐ C ☐

Here's my favourite bird at the zoo! I loved its colourful feathers and its yellow beak, but its claws were quite long and scary!

5 Which bird is the writer describing?

A ☐ B ☐ C ☐

---

6 Read the text and choose the correct answer.

My name is Jen and I'm from the UK. I have two brothers, one is older and one is younger. My big brother is called Brad. He's really ¹____ sport. He always wears ²____ and trainers. He is very confident, but he can be a bit ³____ sometimes. He tells me and my little brother what to do. My younger brother is called Flynn. He is really funny and loves playing games. He's very messy though. He never picks his clothes ⁴____ and he likes listening ⁵____ loud rock music! I'm quite different from my brothers. I'm very quiet, but I'm not ⁶____! My brothers and I have very different personalities, ⁷____ we are still best friends!

1	a on	b into	c with
2	a tracksuits	b uniforms	c shirts
3	a helpful	b clever	c bossy
4	a up	b in	c of
5	a of	b to	c with
6	a bored	b bore	c boring
7	a or	b but	c because

Exam Time 1 — Reading and Writing — Units 1–3

7 Read the texts and answer the questions with A (Andrea), L (Laura), S (Sofia).

1. Who does lots of speaking in their job? ☐
2. Who works with people doing the same job? ☐
3. Who works in a team of people who do different jobs? ☐
4. Who talks about the type of personality you need to do her job? ☐
5. Who needs to show lots of different feelings? ☐
6. Who is still learning about their job? ☐
7. Who says her job is sometimes hard? ☐

Andrea I got my job at the animation company last year. I studied art at university, but I like drawing cartoons more than serious art! I normally draw everything on the computer. I work with lots of other artists and we all draw different things. At the moment, I don't know how to do everything, so I don't draw the main characters! I usually draw things like trees, clouds or buildings. It's still cool to see your drawings in a film, though.

Laura I started working as an actor about twenty years ago. I make lots of films and TV shows every year, but mostly animations, so I don't show my face. I just talk. The interesting thing is that I often act as animals in cartoons! To be an actor on an animation, you need to try to sound happy, sad or excited. You can't use your face or your body! It can be difficult, but it is often very funny.

Sofia I work as a film director at the animation company. I normally take an idea from a writer and make it into a film. I have to plan how I want to show the story in each part of the film. It is very creative work and I spend lots of time with other people. I work with the artists, actors, writers and musicians. To be a director, you need to be hard-working, but also creative and friendly. I love working on animated films and seeing ideas become real!

8 Read the review and complete the notes. Use no more than three words from the text.

What is the name of the Safari Park?

Review of Tabor Safari Park

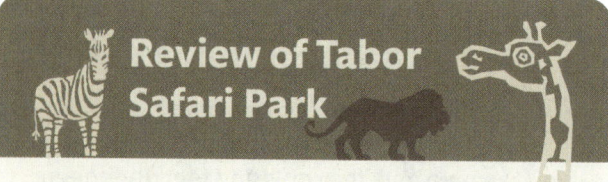

Tabor Safari Park is a great day out for all the family. We took the train at 9 o'clock. Then we walked from the train station to the park. It only takes about 20 minutes.

We spent about an hour walking around the part of the park where the smaller animals and birds live. Then, we went around the other half of the park on a safari bus to look at the big animals. Here there are zebras, giraffes and elephants. I even saw a lion! There are lots of places where you can have a picnic, but we had lunch at the Zebra café. They are building a new vegetarian restaurant in the park.

The park is open every day (except 25 December) from 10 a.m. to 5.30 p.m. It costs £65 for a family of 2 adults and 2 children, or £25 for adults and £15 for children under 16.

Name of Safari Park: [1] _Tabor Safari Park_
How long to walk from the train station: [2] _____
See smaller animals by: [3] _____
See bigger animals by catching: [4] _____
Where to buy food: [5] _____
Closed on: [6] _____
Opens at: [7] _____
Family ticket price: [8] £_____

9 Read the email from your English friend, Grace.

From: Grace

Was Sara's party good last night? I'm sorry I didn't come. I had a bad headache. What did you wear? What present did you buy her?

Write an email to Grace and answer the questions. Write 25–35 words.

Exam Time 2 — Listening — Units 1–6

1 🔊 **ET1–6.1** Listen to Beth talking to her friend, Chris, about a concert. Choose the correct answer.

> **Exam tip**
> Think about the topic of the conversation (in the rubric) and read the questions. What type of vocabulary do you think you will hear?

1. Who went with Chris to the concert?
   a Beth   b Ray   c Brad
2. Which band did Chris like best?
   a Dakota   b The Fireflies
   c Blue Paper
3. Where did Beth see the band before?
   a at a festival   b at a theatre   c on TV
4. Which band member didn't play?
   a Mike   b Joe   c Danny
5. Why did the band member not play?
   a He hurt his back.
   b He had a sore throat.
   c He hurt his head.
6. What time did the concert finish?
   a 11.00 p.m.   b 11.30 p.m.   c 12.00 a.m.

2 🔊 **ET1–6.2** Listen to a man talking about a piece of technology. Complete the notes with the missing information.

> **Exam tip**
> The answers are in order in the recording. Follow carefully, so you know what information you need to listen for next.

A new gadget

Item:	¹ *smartwatch*
When you can buy it:	² from _____
Gives information about:	³ _____
Can work:	⁴ _____
Shop price:	⁵ £ _____
Colours:	⁶ _____

3 🔊 **ET1–6.3** Listen to Kenny talking to a friend about buying things for a new house. Match people 1–6 with things a–h. There are two extra things.

> **Exam tip**
> All options from the list a–h are in the recording, even the ones you don't need. Listen carefully to choose the correct ones.

PEOPLE
1. ☐ Dad
2. ☐ Mum
3. ☐ Kenny
4. ☐ Elsa
5. ☐ Helena
6. ☐ Harry

THINGS
a armchair
b bed
c bookcase
d curtains
e fridge
f games console
g rug
h TV

4 🔊 **ET1–6.4** Listen. Then listen again and write down what you hear during each pause.

> **Exam tip**
> If you miss a word, leave a space. At the end, read the sentence and use your knowledge to try to guess what the word might be.

Exam Time 2 Reading and Writing Units 1–6

5 Read the texts and choose the correct answer.

Exam tip
Think about why answers are wrong as well as why the answer you choose is right.

1 I'm a friendly, local teenager and I love dogs! If you need someone to walk your dogs in the evenings or at the weekend, call Charlie on **0729853748**.

Charlie:
- a wants to have her own dog.
- b offers to walk dogs any day.
- c can look after dogs in your house.

2 I used to feel tired all the time and always had coughs and colds. Now I drink VeggieJuice every day and I feel great!

The writer:
- a feels better now.
- b wants to know how to be healthy.
- c has 'VeggieJuice' when they are ill.

3 Hi Theo,
Can you bring the laptop charger that I left at your house to school tomorrow, please? My laptop battery is dying! Thanks, Oliver

Oliver needs to:
- a buy a new laptop charger.
- b use Theo's laptop charger.
- c charge his laptop.

4 Lee Park Basketball team
We are looking for new players to join our friendly team! You don't need to know how to play, we can teach you. We train on a Tuesday afternoon and Saturday morning every week.

- a The team plays twice a week.
- b A new basketball team is starting.
- c You must be able to play basketball to join the team.

5 Amina, did you use my tablet? I wanted to play a game, but the touchscreen isn't working. I told you not to touch it! Zara

Zara:
- a wants to use Amina's tablet.
- b thinks Amina broke her tablet.
- c needs Amina to help her with her tablet.

6 Sorry, I can't come to the cinema tonight. I have a really bad headache. I think I listened to too much loud music after school. Ann

Ann:
- a doesn't feel well, so she can't go out tonight.
- b went to a concert after school.
- c wants to go the cinema on a different day.

6 Read the article and choose the correct answer.

Would you like to ¹____ your lights on just by speaking? Would you like a mirror that gives information about your health? No, this is not a home of the future, these are things that you ²____ buy now. Smart ³____ are one of the most popular pieces of technology for homes. They can ⁴____ music, tell you about the weather and even ⁵____ to other things in the house like your oven, heating or phone. There are also new smart ⁶____. They can tell you if your food is getting old, order more food and even give you ideas for meals by looking at the things inside.
So, would you like to have a house full of technology?

1 a make   b check   c switch
2 a must   b can   c have to
3 a speakers b headsets   c devices
4 a give   b play   c save
5 a send   b connect   c upload
6 a fridges   b screens   c computers

Exam Time 2   Reading and Writing   Units 1–6

7 Complete the email with one word in each gap.

> **Exam tip**
> Decide if you need to find a verb, a noun, an adjective, an article or something else.

To: terry@hello.com

Hi Terry,

How are you? ¹_____ you see the doctor yesterday? I hope you're feeling better now. I think I've ²_____ a cold too! Or perhaps it's just hay fever because I sneeze every time I go into the garden. Last year my doctor gave me ³_____ tablets, but I don't always remember ⁴_____ take them!
Yesterday I went to the gym. Martin didn't ⁵_____ with me because he was busy. I did ⁶_____ much exercise and I hurt my shoulder. I have to rest it ⁷_____ the moment. This is NOT a good week!
Anyway, it's time to finish. I ⁸_____ do some homework!

Love,
Amanda

8 Read the advert and answer the questions.

> **Exam tip**
> Highlight the question words. This will help you to focus on the type of information you need to find.

ROOM AVAILABLE Large double bedroom with bathroom.

You will share the kitchen, living room and garden with three other students. The room has a bed and wardrobe, but you will need to bring a desk, curtains and any other furniture you need.

The house is near the library and is a fifteen-minute bus ride to the shopping centre.

The room is available from next month and is £88 a week. If you need parking for your car you can pay an extra £25 a month.

For more information, please call 0725372833.

1 What type of room is it?
   double room with bathroom
2 Who else lives in the house?
   _____
3 What is there in the room?
   _____
4 What is the house close to?
   _____
5 When can people move in?
   _____
6 How much is the room?
   _____

9 Last week you were playing basketball. Look at the pictures and write a description of what happened for your diary. Write 80–100 words in your notebook.

Exam Time 3 Listening   Units 1–9

1 🔊 ET1–9.1 Listen and choose the correct answer.

> **Exam tip**
> Read the questions and highlight key words in them before listening for the first time.

1. What was the weather like on the boy's holiday?
   A ☐   B ☐   C ☐

2. What is near the boy's home?
   A ☐   B ☐   C ☐

3. What is the boy's problem?
   A ☐   B ☐   C ☐

4. How much was the girl's laptop?
   A ☐ £500   B ☐ £1000   C ☐ £1500

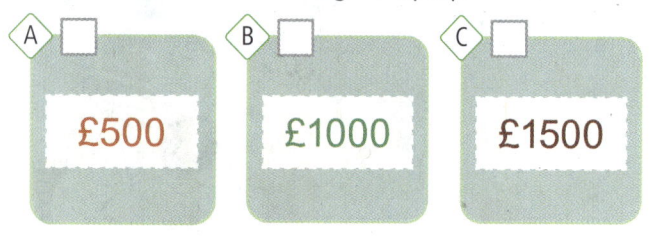

5. What does the girl have to do after school?
   A ☐   B ☐   C ☐

6. When did the girl move to this town?
   A ☐ OCTOBER   B ☐ MARCH   C ☐ JUNE

2 🔊 ET1–9.2 Listen to a girl talking to her friend about a summer job. Complete the notes with the missing information.

SUMMER JOB

Work until: [1] *15 September*
Place: [2] _____ shop
Where: [3] the _____ Centre
Pay: [4] £_____ per hour
Phone number: [5] _____
Speak to: [6] Mr _____

3 🔊 ET1–9.3 Listen and choose the correct answer.

1. You will hear a girl and a boy talking about looking after a cat.
   What shouldn't the boy do?
   a give the cat too much food
   b play with the cat
   c brush the cat

2. You will hear a girl and a boy talking about buying something.
   What does the boy offer to do?
   a give the girl some money
   b buy the girl a magazine
   c go to the shop

3. You will hear two friends talking about a jacket.
   Where was the shop where the girl bought her jacket?
   a close to the baker's
   b in the shopping centre
   c near the bank

4. You will hear a boy and a girl talking about films.
   What is the girl's favourite film?
   a *Aliens of New York*   b *The Boat*
   c *Wild People*

5. You will hear friends talking about jobs.
   What is the boy's dad's job?
   a musician   b receptionist
   c doctor

4 🔊 ET1–9.4 Listen. Then listen again and write down what you hear during each pause.

Exam Time 3 — Reading and Writing — Units 1–9

5 Read the text and choose the correct answer.

A World Family

People often ask Anna, Jan and Lise De Jong where they live and they answer nowhere! That's because they spend their lives moving around the world. 'We've always liked travelling,' says Anna De Jong. 'I met Jan in Sydney. He is from the Netherlands and was on holiday. I come from the UK and was visiting family.'

The De Jong family aren't the only travelling family. More and more people are leaving their homes, schools and jobs to travel. 'When Lise was small, we lived in London. We both worked in offices and always felt tired. We also often had coughs and colds. We wanted to do something different with our lives, so we decided to travel for a year,' Anna says. 'But we never stopped travelling!' laughs Jan. How is this life possible though? Firstly, the De Jong parents teach Lise. 'I learn about the history, culture and language of the place we are in,' says Lise. 'At the moment, we are in China, so I'm learning Mandarin Chinese. We have also visited the Great Wall and a local school to see how children here learn. Next, we are going to Bangkok. That will be our first time in Thailand. This year, we've already been to Russia and Greece. The family also have to earn some money. 'Both Mum and Dad work, but they don't go to an office. They teach online and have also started a blog giving advice to other travelling families.'

1 Where is Anna from?
   a Australia   b the UK   c the Netherlands
2 Why did the family start travelling?
   a Because they often didn't feel well.
   b Because they lost their jobs.
   c Because they wanted to change their lives.
3 How does Lise learn?
   a She has lessons online.
   b Her parents give her lessons.
   c She goes to school in the country she is in.
4 Which of these places haven't the family visited yet?
   a China   b Thailand   c Russia
5 Which of these jobs do Anna and Jan do now?
   a teachers   b tour guides   c office workers

6 Read the texts and choose the correct answer.

Exam tip
Think about the meaning of the whole text when deciding which word to choose.

1
Your homework is to _____ out more information about the landscape of New Zealand and write a report of 500 words.

   a look   b try   c find

2
_____ WANTED
We are looking for a full-time worker to join the team in our office. You need to be good at maths and managing money. You also need a college diploma.

   a Lawyer   b Accountant   c Chef

3
Escalators → this way
If you prefer to use the _____, it is at the back of the shopping centre.

   a lift   b trolley   c plastic bag

4
Mum, can I _____ £10? I want to go to the cinema tonight. Thanks, Melody

   a lend   b borrow   c save

5
Dear Laurie,
We're having a brilliant time and the weather has been amazing. Tomorrow we are going fishing at the _____ 😉 Miss you! Love,
Alex

   a lake   b valley   c border

6
For the _____ trip, please can you bring: walking boots, a water bottle, food, a compass and a raincoat.
Meet at 9 a.m. in the car park.

   a skiing   b kayaking   c hiking

Exam Time 3 — Reading and Writing — Units 1–9

7 Complete the email with one word in each gap.

> **Exam tip**
> Read the whole text through to understand the topic before you start thinking about what to write in the gaps.

Hi Jacques,

I hope you ¹*are* well. I need some advice! The teacher ² _____ just given us our French test results. My results weren't very good! They're worse ³ _____ last term. I'll have to take another test ⁴ _____ week. So, I would like to ask you ⁵ _____ questions about grammar, please. Can I call you? I really don't understand some of the tenses.

Have you finished your term tests ⁶ _____ ? I hate this time of year! Today is ⁷ _____ hottest day of the year and I want to go to the beach, but I have to stay inside and study ⁸ _____ tests!

Write soon,
Mia

8 Read the article and complete the notes. Use no more than three words from the text.

Harrods

is one of the most famous department stores in the world. It attracts lots of celebrities. There are seven floors and 330 different departments! Harrods employs more than 4,000 people and fifteen million customers visit the store every year. You can buy nearly everything there, from T-shirts to houses! In the 1970s, people could buy wild animals such as lions, tigers and even elephants! The shop doesn't have a pet department anymore. When it started in 1849 it only had one room and it didn't sell very much — only tea and groceries. In 1898 it was one of the first places in the world that had an escalator.

1 Harrods is a very *famous* shop.
2 Many _____ shop there.
3 Over _____ work at Harrods.
4 Harrods used to sell _____.
5 The shop opened in the year _____.
6 At the beginning, there was only _____ at Harrods.

9 Read the blog about saving money and choose the correct answer.

Next year I want to travel to Italy to visit the ¹____ because I really want to learn to ski. There is only one problem, it's going to be ²____! So, this year I need to try to ³____ lots of money, so I can pay for the flights. The first thing I'm going to do is to look for a part-time job. I'm going to ask if they need any shop ⁴____ in the shopping centre. Next, I'm going to look at all my old clothes and games, and ⁵____ them online. Finally, I'm going to try really hard to save my ⁶____ money. This means not ⁷____ money on things I don't need!

	a	b	c
1	coast	mountains	capital city
2	expensive	cheap	quality
3	pay	save	borrow
4	customers	people	assistants
5	use	sell	get
6	extra	pocket	bank
7	using	taking	spending

> **Exam tip**
> Remember to answer ALL the questions in the email.

10 Imagine you are on holiday in a natural place (the mountains, a beach, a lake, etc.). Write a message to a friend.

Tell them:
- where you are and what it is like.
- what activities you have already done.
- what your plans are.

Write 50–70 words in your notebook.

Self-checks answer key

Unit 1 Self-check

Exercise 1
1 comics   2 classical   3 actor   4 romantic
5 animated   6 salsa

Exercise 2
1 playing   2 listening   3 taking   4 reading
5 watching   6 drawing

Exercise 3
1 phone-ins   2 message board
3 Current affairs   4 news headlines
5 weather forecast   6 documentaries
7 video clips   8 reality shows

Exercise 4
1 Where do you live?
2 Does your dad work every day?
3 How many English lessons do you have a week?
4 Do you go swimming every Saturday?
5 How often do you take photos?

Exercise 5
1 e   2 d   3 c   4 b   5 a

Exercise 6
1 don't like   2 Do you want   3 doesn't live
4 doesn't speak   5 gives

Exercise 7
1 How   2 problem   3 opinion   4 ask
5 good

Unit 2 Self-check

Exercise 1
1 uniform   2 trainers   3 earrings   4 cotton
5 belt   6 scarf   7 shorts

Exercise 2
1 annoying   2 tired   3 boring   4 interesting
5 embarrassed   6 excited   7 relaxing

Exercise 3
1 tidy   2 chatty   3 kind   4 clever   5 rude
6 bossy

Exercise 4
1 's/is wearing   2 's/is Mike going
3 'm/am not doing   4 Is Dan driving
5 isn't/is not working … 's/is sleeping
6 's/is sitting   7 isn't/is not eating

Exercise 5
1 are you doing   2 read   3 I'm trying
4 don't want   5 I always wear
6 Are you going   7 am doing

Exercise 6
1 a   2 b   3 a   4 a   5 b

Unit 3 Self-check

Exercise 1
1 snake   2 polar bear   3 horse   4 chicken
5 rabbit   6 claw   7 fur   8 feathers

Exercise 2
1 aggressive   2 sociable   3 playful
4 adventurous   5 lively

Exercise 3
1 buy   2 brush   3 put   4 feed   5 train
6 take   7 spend

Exercise 4
1 was   2 Were   3 wasn't   4 Was   5 was

Exercise 5
1 didn't like   2 did you go
3 didn't work   4 didn't answer
5 Did the teacher teach

Exercise 6
1 wasn't   2 wasn't   3 Did   4 didn't
5 stayed

Exercise 7
1 so … mean … mind
2 feel … No

Unit 4 Self-check

Exercise 1
1 console   2 charger   3 handsfree headset
4 keyboard   5 digital camera   6 screen
7 smartwatch   8 cable

Exercise 2
1 check   2 play   3 send   4 download
5 make   6 listen   7 search

Exercise 3
1 slow   2 check   3 hung   4 Switch   5 try

Exercise 4
1 used to play   2 didn't use to play
3 Did … use to give   4 used to write
5 didn't use to go   6 Did … use to visit
7 didn't use to send

Exercise 5
1 going   2 working   3 to go   4 helping
5 to learn   6 to feed   7 to find   8 reading

Exercise 6
1 charge   2 switch   3 calling   4 search
5 online

Unit 5 Self-check

Exercise 1
1 a   2 a   3 c   4 a   5 c   6 c   7 a

Exercise 2
1 make   2 vacuum   3 do   4 put on
5 tidies   6 took   7 do

Exercise 3
1 gallery   2 station   3 centre   4 hall
5 office   6 information centre

Exercise 4
1 where   2 who   3 which   4 that   5 who
6 where   7 which   8 that

Exercise 5
1 can   2 can   3 mustn't   4 can't   5 has to
6 mustn't   7 have to

Exercise 6
1 give me some advice
2 Where do you think   3 that's a good idea
4 Why don't you go   5 Thanks for the advice

Unit 6 Self-check

Exercise 1
1 stomach   2 skin   3 brain   4 ankle
5 muscles   6 toes   7 elbow   8 knee

Exercise 2
1 c   2 a   3 b   4 c   5 b   6 b

Exercise 3
1 temperature   2 allergy   3 hay
4 headache   5 throat   6 flu

Exercise 4
1 much   2 many   3 any   4 lot   5 isn't
6 some   7 many   8 enough

Exercise 5
1 saw   2 was reading   3 came
4 Were you waiting   5 weren't   6 Were you
7 remembered

Exercise 6
1 matter … feel … should
2 feeling … hurts

Unit 7 Self-check

Exercise 1
1 box … bakery   2 packet … newsagent's
3 bottle … pharmacy   4 pair … shoe shop

Exercise 2
1 escalator   2 trolley   3 court
4 department   5 toilets   6 shopper
7 park   8 multi-screen

Exercise 3
1 pocket   2 change   3 price   4 offer
5 money   6 wallet   7 bag   8 recycle

Exercise 4
1 more boring   2 bigger
3 the most enjoyable   4 as big
5 the cheapest   6 the most difficult
7 as nice   8 the kindest

Exercise 5
1 am seeing   2 are going to visit
3 Are you coming   4 is going to ask
5 'm/am going to buy   6 is playing
7 'm/am not going

Exercise 6
1 Can   2 ones   3 try   4 take   5 change

Unit 8 Self-check

Exercise 1
1 journalist   2 care worker   3 accountant
4 gardener   5 architect   6 tour guide

Exercise 2
1 for   2 in   3 as   4 on   5 earn   6 in   7 in
8 for

Exercise 3
1 pupils   2 staff   3 head   4 playground
5 library   6 classmates

Exercise 4
1 won't be … 'll/will watch
2 Will you stay
3 won't get … 'll/will be
4 will be … 'll/will be able
5 Will you be, 'll/will phone
6 won't finish

Exercise 5
1 Will   2 go   3 gets   4 will you   5 don't

Exercise 6
1 We will definitely be   2 I probably won't   3 They might arrive   4 Will you definitely come   5 She might not want

Unit 9 Self-check

Exercise 1
1 beach   2 river … fields   3 island   4 city
5 mountain   6 flag   7 lake

Exercise 2
1 cycling   2 scuba diving   3 windsurfing
4 snowboarding   5 surfing   6 climbing
7 swimming

Exercise 3
1 life jacket   2 kayak   3 paddle
4 helmet   5 goggles   6 map

Exercise 4
1 have (never) forgotten
2 has (already) written
3 have (already) seen
4 has (already) drunk
5 has (already) left
6 have (never) bought
7 Have (you) done
8 have (just) arrived

Exercise 5
1 Have you seen   2 haven't had
3 've just spoken   4 has already bought
5 Have you ever worked
6 have never been
7 Have you ever seen

Exercise 6
1 Can … course
2 for … go
3 mind

Pearson Education Limited
KAO Two
KAO Park
Hockham Way
Harlow, Essex
CM17 9SR
England
and Associated Companies throughout the world.

pearsonenglish.com/widerworld2e

© Pearson Education Limited 2022

All rights reserved; no part of this publication may be reproduced, stored in a retrieval system, or transmitted in any form or by any means, electronic, mechanical, photocopying, recording, or otherwise without the prior written permission of the Publishers.

First published 2022

ISBN: 978-1-292-42278-7

Set in Frutiger Next Pro
Printed in Mexico

Acknowledgements

The Publishers would like to thank all the teachers and students around the world who contributed to the development of Wider World Second Edition: Milena Aleksić, Tuğba Arslantaş, Gülşah Aslan, Mahgol Baboorian, Katarzyna Beliniak, Burcu Candan, Seri Diri, Hanna Dudich, Sema Karapinar, Nadiia Kasianchuk, Duygu Kayhan, Iryna Kharchenko, Ana Krstić, Ilknur Manav, Fulya Mertoğlu, Ivana Nikolov, Banu Oflas, Duygu Özer, Jagoda Popović, Marija Šanjević, Karmen Irizar Segurola, Elif Sevinç, Ludmila Shengel, Ayşe Sönmez, Anna Standish, Natalia Tkachenko, Pamela Van Bers, Jelena Vračar, Agnieszka Woźnicka, Münevver Yanık.

The Publishers would like to thank the following people who commented on the Wider World Second Edition content: Milena Aleksić, Mahgol Baboorian, Hanna Dudich, Izabela Kołando, Karmen Irizar Segurola, Joanna Srokosz, Anna Zając.

We would also like to thank the authors of the first edition of Wider World whose work has been the basis for creating this adaptation: Kathryn Alevizos, Carolyn Barraclough, Catherine Bright, Sheila Dignen, Lynda Edwards, Rod Fricker, Suzanne Gaynor, Bob Hastings, Jennifer Heath, Liz Kilbey, Stuart McKinlay, Sarah Thorpe, Tasia Vassilatou, Damian Williams, Sandy Zervas.

Photo Acknowledgements

123RF.com: alexytrener 33, Andriy Popov 48, 106, belchonock 53, bryljaev 3, Cathy Yeulet 4, 4, 37, Chon Kit Leong 90, Dmitry Kalinovsky 81, domenicogelermo 6, dotshock 4, Filip Fuxa 94, Helen Hotson 91, 97, Iakov Kalinin 90, imagesource 4, iriana88W 105, istill 4, Jaap Bleijenberg 29, Jacek Chabraszewski 4, Juan Jose Simon LLerena 9, Kaspars Grinvalds 80, Kittipong Jirasukhanont 41, lightfieldstudios 11, meinzahn 87, michaeljung 11, nd3000 70, Noriko Cooper 61, saphire 38, scabrail 3, Sean Pavone 93, shutswis 38, vectorikart 5; **Alamy Stock Photo:** Manfred Gottschalk 19; **Getty Images:** AleksandarGeorgiev/E+ 42, Alistair Berg/Photodisc 70, Artem Varnitsin/EyeEm 39, Atlantide Phototravel/Corbis Documentary 73, BJI/Blue Jeans Images 50, Burak Karademir/Moment 83, Carina König 60, Chris Ryan/OJO Images 80, Compassionate Eye Foundation/Stone 85, David C Tomlinson/The Image Bank 65, Enrico Calderoni/Alfo 68, Fabio Formaggio/EyeEm 11, Fuse/Corbis 43, GCShutter/E+ 65, hadynyah/E+ 19, Hill Street Studios/DigitalVision 80, Igor Alecsander/E+ 9, Image Source 63, 86, JGI/Tom Grill 59, Jose Luis Pelaez Inc/DigitalVision 13, 53, 80, kali9/E+ 12, Kentaroo Tryman/Maskot 52, Martinns/E+ 53, nicolamargaret/E+ 11, PeopleImages/E+ 80, Peter Starman/Photodisc 27, RichLegg/E+ 11, sarra22/E+ 59, SDI Productions/E+ 32, simonkr/E+ 11, skynesher/E+ 59, Solveig Faust/EyeEm 53; **Pearson Education Ltd:** 36, 68, 100, Sophie Bluy 17, Studio 8 44; **Shutterstock.com:** 51, aastock 23, Africa Studio 11, AJR_photo 23, Alex Kuzovlev 38, Alexandra Lande 93, Allik 93, Andresr 80, Andrew Sutton 29, Andrey Pavlov 26, Andriy Solovyov 26, anyaivanova 80, Ayman alakhras 48, Bizroug 70, bmphotographer 26, Bomshtein 3, Bryan Busovicki 36, Chaivit Chana 90, Dean Bertoncelj 26, Dmitry Kalinovsky 80, Dorn1530 3, Dragon Images 53, ElenaKor 70, FiledImage 70, Fotaw 48, Fotokostic 59, Frank L Junior 90, GagliardiImages 75, Galina Barskaya 4, Giedriusok 70, Gita Kulinitch Studio 70, GraphicWorlds 26, HandmadePictures 70, Iryna Inshyna 37, Izmael 93, Jan Bures 29, kibri_ho 48, Lapina 9, Lordn 4, Maksim Kabakou 38, Mandy Godbehear 9, Marcin Niemiec 100, marslander 3, metamorworks 11, Mohamed Rageh 26, Naphat_Jorjee 49, nevodka 90, nito 38, Olena Yakobchuk 37, Olga Kovalenko 48, Ostill is Franck Camhi 55, ozanuysal 3, Pakhnyushchy 90, pavel068 53, Pix11 48, Platslee 90, Pressmaster 96, puwanai 19, Quang Ho 3, Regien Paassen 93, Rido 19, Ridvan Ozdemir 11, Rob Hainer 26, Rob Marmion 83, Rozhnovskaya Tanya 48, Samot 95, Sasa Prudkov 9, Sean McD 3, Seregam 3, Sergey Peterman 38, Sergey Ryzhov 71, Sergiy Kuzmin 38, smereka 26, Southtownboy Studio 45, Steve Bower 19, Syda Productions 70, taelove7 38, takayuki 7, Tan Kian Khoon 70, Venus Angel 48, Vibrant Image Studio 90, Waj 93, wavebreakmedia 37

Illustrated by Laura Arias (Beehive Illustration) 31; Tim Bradford (IllustrationX) 49,102,103,108; Emmanuel Cerisier 68; Amber Day (IllustrationX) 70,72,106; Gergely Fórizs (Beehive Illustration) 101; Stephen Jones 36; Fabián Mezquita 100; Amit Tayal (Beehive Illustration) 58,86,107; Rupert Van Wyk (Beehive Illustration) 5l, 21

All other images © Pearson Education

Cover photo © Front: **Alamy Stock Photo:** Panoramic Images